Caring
God's Way

Caring God's Way

Interactive Course Textbook

Compiled/Developed by Trevor J. Partridge

CWR, Waverley Abbey House, Waverley Lane, Farnham, Surrey GU9 8EP, England

Caring God's Way
Copyright © CWR 2000. Reprinted 2003, 2004

Design and typesetting: CWR Production and START
Cover photograph: Roger Walker
Photographs inside publication: *Learning to Care* video by Scope
Printed in Finland by WS Bookwell
ISBN 1-85345-168-1

Previous editions published as *Learning to Care*, copyright © 1996

Programme 1
Caring: What It's All About

Programme 2
Caring: How To Begin

Programme 3
Caring: The Bible – Our Basis

Programme 4
Caring: Applying Biblical Truth – Sensitively

Programme 5
Caring: Triggering A Change

Programme 6
Caring: A Whole New Perspective

Introduction

Our aim at Waverley Abbey House is to produce quality training resources for the local church and wider Christian community, particularly in the area of Pastoral Care and Counselling. The purpose of this training course on caring is to provide you with a tool that will support and equip your local church to more effectively care for its people and demonstrate to the world the love of Christ.

This six-week interactive course textbook accompanies the video programme entitled "Christian Caring" which is presented by Selwyn Hughes and Trevor J. Partridge. The material was first presented in a series of live seminars to over 80,000 people and has been re-designed into this current video training course format. Our desire is that not only will you be better equipped to care having completed the course, but that the truth of God's Word and the work of the Holy Spirit will touch you deeply. Our prayer is that the course will be a rich spiritual experience for you where you will find your heart touched and you will feel yourself growing in God.

Each of the sessions have five elements to them:

1 Video Presentation

2 Care Group Discussion

3 Personal Study

4 Care Group Review

5 Care Practical Application

Video Presentation

These vary in length from about 30 to 45 minutes and will be viewed by the group together. From time to time graphics appear on the screen on a green background with a red pen. This signifies that there is a space in your textbook notes to be filled in. When there is a full screen heading with an orange background and music this indicates a new heading in the notes. The notes accompanying the video presentation are an identical summary of what is being presented on the screen. Make sure that everyone can see the screen and is comfortable. We suggest that before you put the video presentation on that you spend a few moments praying together and spending a short time in worship.

Care Group Discussion

After the video has finished, if you are watching with a large group, break down into your smaller groups. (See Group Guidelines.) The purpose of this group activity is to review and clarify the material that has been presented on screen. There is a worksheet in your notes for each session to provide you with a framework for your review together. Each group will have a facilitator whose role is to guide the discussion.

Personal Study

The course is designed for you to continue working with the material throughout the following week and before the next video session. The concepts in the video presentation are taken and developed further with some interactive exercises for you each day for five days. They will take you approximately 45–50 minutes each day and you will need to set a time aside each day to do them. They are an integral part of the course and if not completed you will find it difficult to participate in the group interaction. There are some exercises that are optional but if you have time we recommend that you do all the exercises.

Care Group Review

This is a very strategic element in the course – and each week will commence with the group review. The focus of the group on the first week will be to get to know each other and why you are on the course. The focus in the subsequent weeks will be to discuss together your personal studies and to share your findings. The size of the smaller group activity will be no more than six in a group and no less than four. The same members of the group need to work together in both the group activities each week for the duration of the six-week course. One member of the group will have been appointed as the group facilitator.

Care Practical Application

This is something that every course member will be expected to participate in. The goal of it will be to complement the concepts and skills you are learning by caring for someone of your choice for the duration of the course. Details will be outlined at the end of the first week's Care Group Review.

Active participation in all elements of the course content and activities is strongly encouraged if full benefit is to be derived from the course. We therefore ask everyone embarking on the course to commit themselves fully to it.

Group Guidelines

1 There are two group activities each week, group interaction on the personal studies and group discussions following the video presentation.

2 The same groups will stay together for group activities for the duration of the six-week course, with the group being not bigger than six and no smaller than four.

3 Every member of the group belongs and has a part to play. Encourage and allow each member of the group to make a contribution. If one member of the group dominates, other members of the group should gently point this out to them.

4 One member of the group will have been appointed as a group facilitator. Their role will be to keep the group to the guidelines they will have been given. They will not be there as "the leader" of the group but as a guide.

Course Overview

The course is presented in three stages and is designed around three concepts that are central to Christian caring. The first is the importance of coming alongside someone to give them support and strength at a time of particular need in their life. We describe this as the ministry of encouragement. The second stage following on from support and encouragement is to bring hope and direction to them in the light of grace and truth. We describe this as the ministry of exhortation, which means to build someone up. The third stage is, having supported and encouraged someone, and having sought to build them up with hope and direction in the light of grace and truth we endeavour to bring a new perspective of their life circumstances from God's Word. We describe this as caring through enlightenment. The course is built around these three concepts and their interrelationship to each other.

Course Objectives

1 That you will become a more caring person.
2 That you will be drawn into a closer relationship with the Lord.
3 That your Biblical grasp and understanding of Christian caring will grow.
4 That you will develop a closer relationship with members of your own church.
5 That you will develop new skills and insights to enable you to be a more effective person.

Several things will happen:

1 Some of your knowledge will be reaffirmed, clarified and crystallised.
2 You will be introduced to fresh concepts and ideas.
3 You will be challenged to personally grow and develop further in your Christian walk.
4 You will learn from the experiences of others and be able to contribute from your own life experience.
5 You will gain a greater appreciation of the relevance of God's Word to the circumstances of everyday life.

Programme 1

Caring

What It's All About

Imagine the Ideal Church

In today's Church many voices can be heard emphasising the various aspects of its ministry. And each person has his or her own idea about where the biggest emphasis should be placed. It could be:

- evangelism
- expository preaching
- teaching
- praise and worship
- house groups
- prayer
- fasting

All these ministries are important but it must also be recognised that there is also another significant ministry in the Church. Any church that only has these characteristics has missed the importance of caring for one another.

"And this is his command: to believe in the name of his Son, Jesus Christ, and to love one another as he commanded us." 1 John 3:23

Is it possible that even though we might not fail in our mission to the world, that we fail one another? If the fellowship between Christians who live together in a close community is weak and superficial then somewhere those Christians have missed their way.

However blameless our character, however orthodox our doctrine, however efficient our service – all these things are but the ashes upon a rusty altar if we do not know how to

_____   _____ for one another.

Scripture speaks about this issue with great clarity

1 Corinthians 12:25
Romans 12:13
Philippians 2:1–2

Why Special Emphasis is Given to Caring

There are at least three reasons:

1 People are hurting more than we realise

As people go through life, they are impacted by many life experiences such as:

1 _____

2 _____

3 _____

4 _____

5 _____

6 _____

7 _____

Hurting can have a variety of causes. What can seem trivial to one person can be a mountainous difficulty to another.

2 It is a command of Jesus Christ

Our Lord not only lifts the standards to unbelievable heights but also provides the power by which we reach up to them. Love is a decision and when we avail ourselves of God's power, decide to move toward people and act in loving ways (even though we may not feel like it) then it is quite remarkable how, after a while, our feelings begin to change.

3 The more we care the greater our impact on the world

If all we have to offer the world is just "words" then that will make them feel inferior. If they see, however, that what we say is backed up by a lifestyle of caring for one another, then it will make our message irresistible.

The Ministry of Caring

"This is how all men will know that you are my disciples, because you have such love for one another." John 13:35 (JB Phillips)

Those who have studied the growth and development of the human personality tell us that there are three vital ingredients for helping a person reach maturity. These three elements can be seen at their best in a church where the ministry of caring is in operation:

◆ **Encouragement** – coming alongside a person who is hurting, supporting them in their troubled feelings.

◆ **Exhortation** – helping to bring God's truth from the Bible to bear on the person's situation.

◆ **Enlightenment** – simple process of helping people bring their thinking in line with God's thinking as taught in the Scriptures.

Always remember you cannot exhort an unencouraged person.

Caring begins with encouragement. We can never be fully effective at the other levels of caring if we do not know how to encourage.

Caring by Encouragement

The ministry of encouragement is the support we communicate to people by words, or in other ways, to help them cope with, or overcome, a difficult time or experience in their life. To encourage involves coming alongside someone to support them.

In the New Testament the Greek word used for encouragement is "paraklesis" – to come alongside. This is one of the titles of the Holy Spirit – the divine Paraclete, the One who comes alongside, the Comforter.

It is important to realise that everyone in the body of Christ is called to the ministry of encouragement, and to put it into action as often as possible. The writer of Hebrews makes that very clear:

"Let us consider how we may spur one another on towards love and good deeds. Let us not give up meeting together, as some are in the habit of doing, but let us encourage one another – and all the more as you see the Day approaching." Hebrews 10:24, 25

Three areas necessary for effective encouragement are:

1 We must have the _____ to encourage:

   "Let us not give up meeting together, as some are in the habit of doing ..."

2 We must _____ the principles of encouraging others:

   "Let us consider how we may spur one another on towards love and good deeds."

3 We must _____ in the ministry of encouragement in an increasing measure:

   "... and all the more as you see the Day approaching."

Common Causes of Discouragement

One of the questions we must ask ourselves if we are to develop the ministry of encouragement is: why do people have problems? What are people struggling with at the core of their beings? Understanding this enables us to "scratch where people itch".

There are many causes of discouragement, such as unhelpful words and an insensitive or uncaring attitude.

One of the foremost reasons has to do with the

_____

People become deeply discouraged when they think that if they were to share what they really think and feel they will not be accepted as they are.

How Human Problems Began (Genesis 3)

In the Garden of Eden, Adam and Eve enjoyed unclouded communion with God and experienced joyful acceptance.

Sin, however, brought chaos into their lives, and gave rise to a completely new emotion which they had not experienced before, anxiety and fear.

Adam explained this strange behaviour by saying, "I was afraid ... because I was naked". This has reference, not just to physical nudity, but to the problem of emotional and spiritual exposure and rejection.

Every one of us has a similar fear – the fear that if people see our emotional nakedness they will not accept us as we are. So we try to protect ourselves from such vulnerability by layers of protection.

A layer is anything we pull around us to avoid the possibility of rejection.

In an effort to avoid dealing with what he feared, Adam chose to hide, and by doing so employed the world's first layers of protection.

From that day to this, mankind has searched for ways to cover up their deep feelings of worthlessness, insecurity, inferiority and insignificance. The human personality is extremely adept at finding ways to protect itself against the fear of exposure and rejection.

Role Play: Layer to Layer Fellowship

Ten protective layers

1 _____

2 _____

3 _____

4 _____

5 _____

6 _____

7 _____

8 _____

9 _____

10 _____

How do we encourage people to come out from behind their layers of protection:

_____ **and** _____

When Christians attempt to develop rapport with each other from behind their defensive position, all they succeed in doing is experiencing a superficial type of fellowship which does little to commend itself to the outside world.

People need to be sure that when they come out from behind their layers of protection that they will not be rejected.

Without understanding and without acceptance, therefore, there really can be no encouragement.

IN SUMMARY

Reasons for Caring

People hurt more than we realise

It is an express command of Jesus Christ

The more we care the greater the impact on the world

Levels of Caring

Encouragement supports feelings

Exhortation influences behaviour

Enlightenment changes thinking

Keys to Caring

Begin with encouragement

Show understanding

Demonstrate acceptance

CARE GROUP DISCUSSION

In your small groups review the video using the following questions to stimulate your discussion. They are only guidelines to help you think through what you have viewed.

Remember! The goal here is to review the video material together.

1 Is it right to say that caring is a neglected ministry?

2 Which are the most prominent ministry emphases in our church?

3 Are the people in the video typical of an average church?

4 Talk through the Biblical basis for caring.

5 Discuss the 3 areas suggested as essential to maturity.

6 Talk through the concept of encouragement.

7 Are the layers of protection mentioned typical?

8 Is discouragement spiritual or psychological?

Don't worry if you have not covered all the questions.

Caring

What It's All About

Week 1 – Personal Study

PERSONAL STUDY – Introduction

Now that you have viewed the video material and had the opportunity to think through its content with your group, you have the opportunity of working with the material on your own. The goal of these studies is to help you think about the concepts a little further and to interact with them by making your own responses and comments. The daily exercises in the textbook are an integral part of the course to help you get the best out of it.

1   The studies are designed to be completed one a day over a five-day period – it can be any five days you choose between the video showings, which will usually be weekly. Resist the temptation of leaving it to the last minute and then trying to do several together.

2   The exercises will probably take between 45–50 minutes. It is important that you do not rush through them, so set an hour aside each day and try not to allow interruptions to distract you. Before you commence the study it will be helpful to review the page in your video notes that it relates to.

3   Each day's exercise commences with a Bible reading and concludes with a prayer. It will be good to pray before you commence and you may feel it appropriate to pray at different points during the study.

4   There are Scripture references, referred to throughout, and it is important that you look up all Scripture references and read them. Some of the answers will be dependent on them.

5   As you fill in the responses some will be easier than others. You may find some personally challenging as you are asked to consider how it applies to you. Be as honest as you can, recognising that as we are willing to consider issues in our own lives, and face their challenges, so we are able to further grow and develop in our caring for others.

6   There are some exercises that are optional. They are included because we feel they will be helpful and recommend that if you have the time you complete all the exercises.

7   When you meet again with your group, next week, you will have the opportunity of sharing with them your findings and responses.

Our prayer is that, as you work through these exercises, the Lord will minister to you deeply from His Word, by His Spirit, fully equipping you to be more effective in the ministry of caring.

The Importance of Caring

 Cross reference: video notes pages 11–13

 Reading: John 4:1–26 Woman at the well.

> *Jesus answered, "Everyone who drinks this water will be thirsty again, but whoever drinks the water I give him will never thirst. Indeed, the water I give him will become in him a spring of water welling up to eternal life." John 4:13–14*

This first week we begin to explore the subject of caring. The course is designed around three concepts that are central to Christian caring. The first is the importance of giving support to someone. We describe this as encouragement. The second is bringing hope and direction in the light of grace and truth. We describe this as exhortation and the third is bringing a fresh perspective to life circumstances from God's point of view. We describe this as enlightenment. If we truly care we will want to give others support, hope and a fresh perspective. Over the weeks we will be exploring these concepts more fully, but this week we have commenced with the video presentation on care through encouragement. We can see from our reading today that Jesus in this significant encounter with the woman at the well, gave her support, hope and a new perspective in life.

When we look at Jesus in the Gospels He is always demonstrating a personal involvement with others. He delighted in conversing with people at a close and intimate level. However, when Jesus spoke, it was always with insight, wisdom and care.

Can you think of times where we observe Jesus demonstrating care?

e.g. <u>Widow of Nain</u>   e.g. <u>Dying Thief</u>   _____

_____   _____   _____

Caring is such an important ministry. Strong's concordance tells us the Greek word for "care" means to "care for physically or otherwise, to take care of" and dictionary definitions of "care" encompass – protection, someone to watch over or attend to, to feel concern, sympathetic, tender, warm – which brings to mind Isaiah 40:11 *"He tends his flock like a shepherd: He gathers the lambs in his arms and carries them close to his heart; he gently leads those that have young."*

We have said caring is important because of three reasons. Explore these reasons a little further:

1 People are hurting more than we realise

"They dress the wound of my people as though it were not serious. 'Peace, peace,' they say, when there is no peace." Jeremiah 6:14

Think of some life experiences that often cause people hurt and distress:

_____

_____

_____

What are some of the ways they might try to handle it?

_____

_____

_____

What are some of the life experiences that have caused you personal pain?

_____

_____

_____

What do you feel helped you to cope?

_____

_____

_____

2 It is an express command of Jesus Christ

"My command is this: Love each other as I have loved you." John 15:12

When Paul talks about fulfilling this command to the Corinthians (1 Corinthians 13) what are the practical characteristics of the caring love he expresses?

_____ _____ _____

_____ _____ _____

_____ _____ _____

Does Paul put a greater emphasis on active support or emotional response?

_____

3 Caring is designed to make a significant impact on the world

"By this all men will know that you are my disciples, if you love one another." John 13:35

What are some of the accusations often levelled at the Church by non-believers?

_____

_____

_____

_____

What might be some of the ways the Church could demonstrate care to non-believers?

_____

_____

_____

When we do not care and fail to address the concerns with which people struggle it results in numerous consequences; to name a few – no spiritual appetite, little or no prayer concern, no desire for fellowship, no desire to witness, lack of spiritual motivation. The effectiveness of the Christian Church is dramatically reduced by the number of spiritual "casualties" in its ranks – regularly, thousands of Christians report "unfit for duty". But the Bible tells us *"... Love your neighbour as yourself."* Galatians 5:14; *"But encourage one another daily, ... so that none of you may be hardened by sin's deceitfulness."* Hebrews 3:13.

The Christian Church is Uniquely Designed to Care

Several years ago it was discovered that there are three important ingredients for healthy human development – support, direction and a belief system. It was discovered that where there was not an environment that provided these elements, there would be a strong level of immaturity. What better place outside of the home is there for an environment of a caring, loving community than the Church.

*"But **encourage** one another daily, as long as it is called Today, so that none of you may be hardened by sin's deceitfulness."* Hebrews 3:13

*"Therefore **exhort** one another and edify – strengthen and build up – one another, just as you are doing."* 1 Thessalonians 5:11 (Amplified Bible).

*"I pray also that the eyes of your heart may be **enlightened** in order that you may know the hope to which he has called you, the riches of his glorious inheritance in the saints ..."* Ephesians 1:18

Levels of Caring

ENCOURAGE

a verbal or non-verbal communication that *supports* a person's *feelings* when they are facing or going through difficult circumstances.

EXHORT

bringing a clear sense of hope concerning God's *direction* for life, resulting in *character* development and changed behaviour.

ENLIGHTEN

seeking to bring a new perspective and definite *transformation* from old thinking patterns to new *thinking* patterns.

Complete the following table:

Key Word	Key Function	Key Focus
ENCOURAGE		
	HOPE	
		THINKING

Prayer: **Father, I recognise that care is part of Your Father heart. Thank You for caring enough to send Jesus and thank You Jesus that You cared enough to give Your life for my salvation. Amen.**

Caring By Encouragement

 Cross reference: video notes page 13–14

 Reading: Hebrews 10:19–25

> *"And let us consider how we may spur one another on towards love and good deeds."* Hebrews 10:24

One of the greatest needs people have is to hear words of affirmation and encouragement. It is life giving to the soul. As carers one of the greatest contributions we can make to hurting people is to encourage them.

The key word that is used in the New Testament to describe the ministry of encouragement, as mentioned on the video, is PARAKLESIS – "being called alongside" to bring strength, to bring courage, to be comforting, fortifying and supporting. The English word "encourage" means "to give or inspire courage or confidence/hope into someone."

Write your own definition of encouragement:

_____

_____

_____

In what ways can we display encouragement?

_____

_____

_____

What are some things that have encouraged you?

_____

_____

_____

The essence of encouragement then is having concern for and caring and sharing with each other, 1 Corinthians 12:25 *"so that there should be no division in the body, but that its parts should have equal concern for each other"*. It is God's desire that we reach out towards others to care and encourage – what was His new commandment (John 13:34)?

_____

_____

_____

What is Paul's framework for encouragement – *"And now these three remain: faith, hope and love. But the greatest of these is love."* 1 Corinthians 13:13.

_____ + _____ + _____ = Encouragement

Look again at today's reading, which verses underline this framework?

V _____ Faith

V _____ Hope   = V _____ encouragement

V _____ Love

We could describe caring as being other-centred, by being willing to come alongside, and encouragement as giving the appropriate level of support, affirmation and appreciation.

One of the unsung heroes of the New Testament is Barnabas – *whose name means son of encouragement*. What were some of his characteristics?

Acts 9:26–27   _____

Acts 11:23   _____

Acts 11:24   _____

Acts 11:26   _____

Acts 11:30   _____

Acts 12:25   _____

Acts 15:36–40 _____

Acts 14:22   _____

In a sentence describe Barnabas, son of encouragement:

_____

_____

What was Barnabas full of? _____

In many churches the focus has moved away from being a caring community to being a doing community, solely centring on a continuous round of activity, albeit good activity, leaving many wounded casualties from life's battles uncared for.

How does the writer to the Hebrews address these two issues in verses 24–25?

_____

_____

_____

What did the early Church devote themselves to? Acts 2:42:

_____

_____

List several ways in which you think it is possible to have "fellowship" with someone else:

_____

_____

_____

In what ways does your church "fellowship" currently carry out a ministry of encouragement?

_____

_____

_____

What other ways can you think of that would provide further encouragement in your "fellowship"?

_____

_____

_____

Whatever kind of church life we are involved in, one thing is clear from the New Testament account is that church life involves other people getting together, people in contact with each other. This takes place in large groups, small groups, praise meetings, prayer meetings, Bible studies, church activities, youth groups, etc. If we fail to recognise that when church activity clouds our ability to draw on Christ's resources to effectively support, encourage and care for needy people, then we have failed. The Church is people, God's people. Heaven will be full of people – redeemed people.

Prayer: **Father I thank You for those who have encouraged me in my Christian walk. I ask You to make me an instrument of encouragement in Your hands, so that others might be blessed. Amen.**

Why People Get Discouraged

 Cross reference: video notes pages 14–15

Reading: 1 Kings 18:36–19:21

> *"... He came to a broom tree, sat down under it and prayed that he might die. 'I have had enough, Lord,' he said. 'Take my life; I am no better than my ancestors.'"*
> 1 Kings 19:4

As we journey through life we are affected by many different circumstances, some are pleasant, enjoyable and memorable, but others affect us deeply and cause us to become disheartened, abandoning hope and wanting to give up. Collins Dictionary defines discouragement as "to be deprived of the will to persist in something". As a result of negative life events, we become dispirited and daunted, the wind is taken out of our sails, our dreams are dashed and our hopes are shattered.

Elijah was clearly a man called by God, on a mission serving God, exposing the false religion of the day, calling attention to the true and only God, but he came to a moment of deep discouragement.

What had Elijah just experienced? – 1 Kings 18:38–39:

a great _____

What did this result in? – 1 Kings 19:1–2:

a great _____

What did this produce in Elijah? – 1 Kings 19:3

a great _____

Where did he end up? – 1 Kings 19:4

in a great _____

What was the final outcome? – 1 Kings 19:4

a great _____

What does this show us about our vulnerability to the process of discouragement?

_____

_____

_____

The characteristics of Elijah at this period in his life were that he was fearful, lonely, tired, exhausted, deflated, threatened, depressed. He was clearly

deeply _____

Elijah, the great prophet of Israel, knew what it was to have an encounter with the giant of despair. Sit for a moment in the shade of the broom tree and watch how this devout man of God falls prey to the deepest form of melancholy. The prophet has just experienced a tremendous victory over Ahab and the Baal-worshippers but then the giant of despair is ushered in by Ahab's wife Jezebel. She predicts that Elijah's life will be over within twenty-four hours. Though this mighty man of God has overcome all previous threats, somehow Jezebel's statement finds its mark. Elijah runs for his life. Finally he sinks in utter despair beneath the broom tree and says: *"I've had enough, Lord. Take my life"* (v4). Did God rebuke him? Or tell him how disappointed He was with him? No, He ministered to him by allowing him to take a long rest and providing a meal or two. Later He gave him a close friend by the name of Elisha to encourage him. Gently He prodded the prophet to get a new perspective on things.

As you think through this experience in Elijah's life, what do you consider triggered the chain of events leading to his discouragement?

_____

_____

Clearly the power of words, although not the sole cause of discouragement, plays an important role.

Read:

Proverbs 12:25
Proverbs 18:21
James 3:10

Write out a summary sentence:

_____

_____

_____

What kind of experiences discourage you?

_____

_____

_____

What kind of words do you find discouraging?

_____   _____   _____

_____   _____   _____

God did not deal harshly with Elijah in his deep discouragement. He could have railed at him "Elijah you know better, look at all the miracles I have worked for you. Look at the recent one on Mount Carmel; you should be rejoicing. I've been very good to you, say 'Praise the Lord' you ungrateful servant."

In the video we gave the foremost reason for discouragement as:

_____

How is this borne out in Elijah's experience?

_____

_____

What is your own experience of this? Give an example:

_____

_____

_____

Look through 1 Kings 19:5–21 again and list the elements that God used to encourage the discouraged prophet:

1 He allowed him to have a good _____ verse 5

2 He sent along an encouraging _____ verse 5

3 He provided for him _____ verse 6

4 After eating he had a period of _____ verse 6

5 The angel of the Lord _____ verse 7

6 After eating again he was _____ verse 8

7 The Lord got him to express his feelings by _____ verse 9

8 Elijah's perspective was that he was _____ verses 10,14

9 The Lord spoke to him _____ verse 12

10 God gave him a fresh _____ verses 15–16

11 God brought Elijah's view of himself as being the only one who was loyal to the Lord _____ verse 18

12 God gave him a permanent _____ verse 21

Prayer: **Father help me to understand that even in moments of discouragement You are there. Help me to trust You and have confidence that You will bring me through as You did with Your servant of old. Amen.**

How Human Problems Began

 Cross reference: video notes pages 15–16

 Reading: Genesis 3

> *"He answered, 'I heard you in the garden, and I was afraid because I was naked; so I hid.'"* Genesis 3:10

What is the first thing that God says about man? Genesis 1:27

Man is a bearer of _____

God paid us His highest compliment when He created us after His own likeness. What does it mean to be created in God's image? Write down your thoughts:

_____

_____

_____

Read Genesis 1:10, 12, 18, 21, 25, 31 – What does God declare about His creation?

That it is _____

Read Genesis 2:18 – What does God declare is not good?

To be _____

Before Adam and Eve sinned they enjoyed unbroken communion, fellowship and intimacy with God. There were no barriers, no threats, no anxiety or tension, just the experience of enjoying complete acceptance. In the presence of God there was no glance of disapproval or unacceptability, but the absolute awareness of unconditional love.

What are some of the emotions that you think Adam and Eve experienced?

_____

_____

Once sin entered the personality terrible consequences followed. One result was that there was emotional disintegration, love flowed out and fear and guilt flowed in. These were emotions that Adam and Eve had not previously experienced.

In response to this new emotional turmoil Adam ran and hid himself from God. What question did God ask Adam?

_____

_____

_____

What was Adam's response?

_____

_____

_____

What were the three key elements of his response?

1 I was _____

2 I was _____

3 So I _____

How do you think Adam might have finished these sentences?

1 I was _____ of _____

2 I was _____ and felt _____

3 So I _____ because _____

In the video it stated that the foremost reason for discouragement is the fear of rejection, and we can see from Adam's experience that the fear of rejection is strongly connected to the fear of exposure. In other words people will find out what we are really like and will not like us and may even discard and disown us. John Powell in his book *Why I am afraid to tell you who I am,* put it like this:

"I am afraid to tell you who I am because if I tell you who I am, you may not like who I am, and it's all that I have."

The fear of rejection, failure and exposure are intrinsic to our personality because of the Fall. As we travel through life, life experiences further aggravate and amplify these deep seated fears. Rejection in life occurs when love, affirmation and acceptance are withdrawn. It is the fear of this real possibility that causes people to develop life patterns to compensate for the deep personal pain they often feel as a result.

List some life experiences that compound our fear of exposure, rejection and failure:

e.g. By being ridiculed in front of others _____

_____

_____

Write down a personal life experience when you have felt rejected, or a failure, or emotionally exposed:

_____

_____

_____

Adam dealt with his situation by hiding, but what else did he do? Genesis 3:7:

_____

_____

_____

When we struggle with the discouraging and debilitating feelings of fear, failure, rejection and exposure we develop ways of protecting ourselves. These are described in the video as layers of protection. They are protective strategies we use to help us hold our lives together, ten were mentioned in the video but there are others, can you think of any?

e.g. Name dropping _____

_____

_____

What is the one that you often use?

_____

How would you describe a layer?

_____

_____

_____

When we relate to others from behind our layers, what are some of the things that this produces in our relationships?

e.g. We feel threatened by what others do. _____

_____

_____

Prayer: **Father, so often I struggle with my fear of rejection and take refuge in my layers of protection. Forgive me for not trusting You enough and give me the courage to step from behind my layers of protection. Amen.**

The Climate for Encouragement

 Cross reference: video notes page 16

 Reading: John 8:1–11

> *"'Then neither do I condemn you,' Jesus declared. 'Go now and leave your life of sin.'"* John 8:11

If people are discouraged because of fear and because their layers of protection and defence strategies keep breaking down, it is important that we recognise that the first stage to encouragement is to provide a non-threatening atmosphere and environment that will help them to step from behind their protective walls.

Where and when do you *least* feel afraid of other people?

_____

_____

_____

When and where do you *most* feel afraid of other people?

_____

_____

_____

When and where do you most feel relaxed and safe?

_____

_____

_____

What kind of relational atmosphere and environment do you feel most comfortable in?

_____

_____

_____

In the video presentation we said that there are two important ingredients in developing the right atmosphere and environment in which the process of encouragement can take place:

1 _____

2 _____

This raises the question "If I accept someone as they are, does this imply that I am accepting and endorsing their behaviour?"

Write down your response to this:

_____

_____

_____

What is the difference between

acceptance and approval:

_____

_____

_____

acceptance and agreement:

_____

_____

_____

How did Jesus demonstrate this with the woman in the reading today?

_____

_____

_____

An important element in acceptance is learning to accept people as they are, differentiating between them and their behaviour, remember that Jesus loved this sinful woman, He certainly did not condone her adulterous behaviour, but He did say to her: "*Woman* _____

_____" verses 10–11

"*For God did not send his Son into the world to condemn the world, but to save the world through him*." John 3:17

Jesus accepted her as she was, but loved her too much to let her stay as she was. How might we describe the response of the Pharisees and leaders of the law to this woman?

_____

_____

_____

Before people are willing to come out from behind their layers they need to know that we care, and that we are willing to take time to understand, this begins to provide for them the context for change.

Showing understanding means being willing to take the time to allow a person the opportunity to expose their troubled feelings in a non-judgemental, non-rejecting atmosphere. When people feel that we understand them, they feel supported and cared for. People do not care how much we know, they want to know how much we care. Understanding often offers more encouragement than seemingly good advice, or even immediate apparent answers. The more precise our understanding the more encouraged the person will feel. The person will be saying to themselves "finally I have found someone who understands me".

There are three key elements to help us to demonstrate acceptance and understanding:

1 Recognise a person's intrinsic worth – Read James 3:9;
   Psalm 139:13–18; Matthew 10:30–31. Put this in a sentence:

_____

_____

_____

2 Recognise a person's potential. Read 1 Corinthians 1:26–28; 2 Corinthians 12:9; Jeremiah 29:11. Put this in a sentence:

_____

_____

_____

3 Recognise a person's worthwhile behaviour. Read Philippians 4:8; Philippians 2:3–4; Romans 12:10. Put this in a sentence:

_____

_____

_____

Understanding and accepting a person is one of the most encouraging things that we can do. Remember a person's biggest fear is "If I expose my real self I will be rejected and be a failure." The core of discouragement is fear, rejection and failure, the heart of encouragement is concern, support, understanding and affirmation.

Encouragement is not changing people but supporting them and must not only be expressed in words, but by actions of kindness and love. 1 John 3:18 says "... *let us not love with words or tongue but with actions and in truth".*

Prayer: **Father, make me an instrument of encouragement. Help me to be accepting and understanding, not condemning or judgemental. Amen.**

Care Group Review

Spend 50–60 minutes talking together on the responses you have written down in your own personal study.

Spend about 10–12 minutes for each day with each member of the group having an opportunity to reflect and discuss their responses. Jot down below things that are helpful to you.

Notes on the Discussion

Day 1

_____

_____

_____

Day 2

_____

_____

_____

Day 3

_____

_____

_____

Day 4

_____

_____

_____

Day 5

_____

_____

_____

Conclusions for the week:

_____

_____

_____

_____

_____

_____

Care Practical Application

When working with a course like this, it is important to take the opportunity to apply what you are learning. To help you do this we want to encourage you to prayerfully choose someone to care for during this course, so that you can sensitively apply the principles of caring we are sharing with you. It does not need to be someone who you feel is struggling with a particular problem, but it can be. It could be a husband, wife, family member, church member, friend, neighbour etc.

I choose _____ and, with God's grace, I want to express His love in a deeper way to them by becoming a more caring person towards them.

Care Practical Application Progress

From the beginning of Week Two, at the end of each day's assignment make a note of how and when you will apply what you have learnt to the person whom you have chosen to care for in a deeper way.

Programme 2

Caring

How To Begin

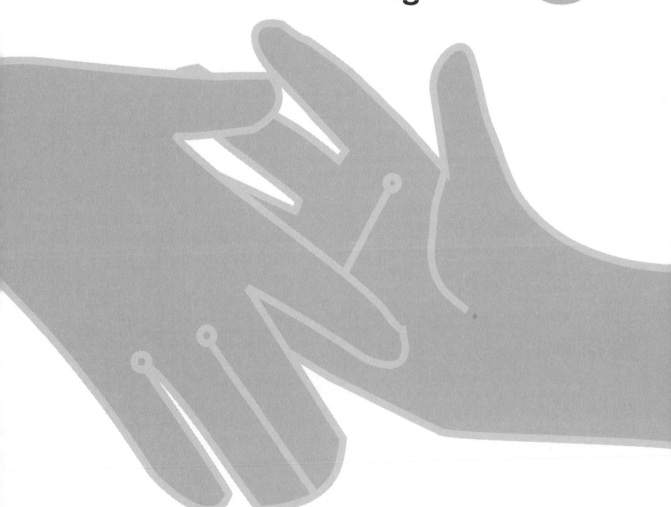

█ A Vital Ministry

Why do you want to be an Encourager?

A number of important principles and skills must be learned if we are to become effective encouragers. Before looking at these in detail, however, we must pause to examine a vital and important issue – motivation.

In 2 Corinthians 5:14, Paul underlines the importance of ministering with the

RIGHT MOTIVE

Our actions should spring from Christ's love and compassion flowing through us in such a way that we want to share it with others – but not for our own self interest or to meet some need in us (1 Corinthians 4:5).

We are told that everything that is not done with a single eye to God's glory will be "burned up" in that day when our ministries will be examined and reviewed.

True Christian caring begins by focusing on at least two things:

1   God's care for you

2   Committing yourself more to serving than being served

"Do nothing out of selfish ambition or vain conceit, but in humility consider others better than yourselves. Each of you should look not only to your own interests, but also to the interests of others." Philippians 2:3–4

█ Be Alert for Opportunities

Encouragement is more effective when the opportunity is seized rather than created. Almost every time we meet in church we miss opportunities to encourage others because we do not know how to recognise the symptoms that hurting people send out. If we are committed to serving, opportunities will begin to reveal themselves every day. Remember that people are often hurting more than we realise.

Many of them are sending out signals which communicate precisely that.

Be on the look out for _____

Such as:

◆ Uncharacteristic behaviour
◆ Letting routine tasks go
◆ Indecisiveness
◆ Tone of voice
◆ Changes in attention given to appearance

Develop your awareness of signals that others send out.

Learn How to Listen

Most of us are better talkers than listeners. Good listening takes practice and involves the following:

1 Be more _____ of the other person than you are of yourself.

2 Don't be _____ about what you are going to say next until the other person has finished talking.

3 Focus on the _____ that lie buried beneath the words.

Empathise with Hurt Feelings

Empathy is feeling with someone, not ignoring or riding roughshod over their feelings, or making light of them. Someone has described it as "your pain in my heart". When someone senses we have time to identify and understand how they are feeling, they feel cared for and supported.

You may know a person's thoughts, judgements and ideas, but you will never truly know a person until you know how he or she really **feels.** Hebrews 4:15 (AV)

Tuning into a person's thoughts and ideas will give you insight into a person's mind, but understanding their true feelings will show you what's in their heart.

Shirley:

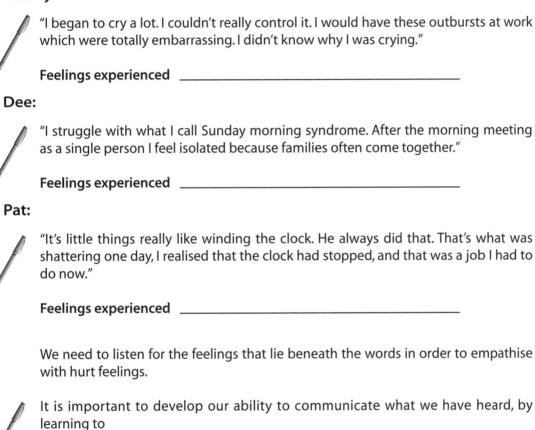

"I began to cry a lot. I couldn't really control it. I would have these outbursts at work which were totally embarrassing. I didn't know why I was crying."

Feelings experienced _____

Dee:

"I struggle with what I call Sunday morning syndrome. After the morning meeting as a single person I feel isolated because families often come together."

Feelings experienced _____

Pat:

"It's little things really like winding the clock. He always did that. That's what was shattering one day, I realised that the clock had stopped, and that was a job I had to do now."

Feelings experienced _____

We need to listen for the feelings that lie beneath the words in order to empathise with hurt feelings.

It is important to develop our ability to communicate what we have heard, by learning to

_____   _____

The Awesome Power of Words

Be aware of the awesome power of words to encourage or discourage, even when expressed with the best intentions.

"The tongue has the power of life and death ..." Proverbs 18:21

"With the tongue we praise our Lord and Father, and with it we curse men who have been made in God's likeness." James 3:9

When confronted by other people's hurt we might find it an uncomfortable experience and feel we don't know what to say.

In this situation try to avoid religious clichés such as:

> "You need to have more faith" or "Praise the Lord anyway"

The effect on the hurting individuals can be very negative. To be an effective encourager we need to use the right words.

The key message we need to communicate is

I'm a _____ and I _____

The careful and effective choice of words is encouraged by Scripture:

Proverbs 12:25
Proverbs 15:4

WORDS that encourage are:

Prompted by love (Proverbs 15:23)

Chosen with care (Proverbs 25:11)

Spoken with tenderness (Ephesians 4:29)

Learn How to Use Words as Door Openers

Door opening is an important technique and ought to be practised by every encourager.

As you listen beneath the words, what do you hear? When your spiritual aerial picks up a possible problem, learn to respond with a door opener and not a door closer.

A *door opener* encourages the other person to open up and usually takes the form of a question that enables a person to share their thoughts.

A *door closer* is usually a statement that causes a person to close up and mostly invites only a one word response.

Good door openers encourage further sharing of the person's feelings. But never *force* a person to share more than they wish. Simply offer yourself – no more.

Understand the Importance of Body Language

More and more studies show that it is not just what we say that is important, but also the way we say it.

Your body language also speaks volumes and can confirm or contradict what you are saying. Let your body communicate your sincerity and interest.

Things to consider in this area are:

◆ **Focus fully on the person**

◆ **Respect psychological space**

◆ **Maintain appropriate posture**

◆ **Use proper and appropriate eye contact**

◆ **Match facial expressions**

Don't feel that in a conversation your role is to solve the problem – in particular don't be drawn in out of your depth.

IN SUMMARY

Six Key Points for Encouragers to Develop:

1 Be alert for opportunities to encourage
2 Learn the art of effective listening
3 Empathise with hurt feelings
4 Use the right words
5 Learn the use of door openers
6 Understand the importance of body language

Don't be drawn in out of your depth – don't feel you must be the answer to the problem.

Some practical forms of encouragement that you can give:

◆ **Clarify the issue**
◆ **Suggest a direction in which the person can go**
◆ **Express your care, support and understanding**

Remember: The essence of encouragement is giving support not answers.

Effective caring is not a single event – it is a process, it does not begin and end in a day.

The Power of Prayer

Your great strength as a Christian carer is the power of prayer. However limited your people-helping skills, there is one thing that every Christian can do for another and that is to pray. But remember, the importance of words:

Pray Naturally   –   in language that is conversational and real

Pray Perceptively –   bringing out the circumstances and feelings
                              that the person has expressed

Pray Specifically –   be clear about what you are asking God to do

When the ministry of care is active and operates in a context of prayer, you will find a climate of:

◆ spiritual growth

◆ openness of heart

◆ a situation in which hurt will surface more easily

Where encouragement doesn't happen in the Church there are at least three consequences

1   A minimum impact of truth

2   People will feel intimidated by truth

3   Complacency and indifference

A local church which takes the time and trouble to teach its people the importance of encouragement will add greatly to the effectiveness of its other ministries. Growth and maturity are more easily reached in the context of good relationships.

CARE GROUP DISCUSSION

In your small groups review the video material using the following questions to stimulate your discussion. They are only guidelines to help you think through what you have viewed.

Remember! The goal here is to review the video material together.

1 **Think through together the issue of motives.**

2 **Talk through the opportunities that exist.**

3 **Explore the issues of listening.**

4 **Explore the power of words.**

5 **What did you feel about the concept of door openers?**

6 **What can be learned from body language?**

7 **Discuss the twin concept of care and prayer.**

8 **Discuss any other items in the video presentation.**

Don't worry if you have not covered all the questions.

Programme 2

Caring

How To Begin

Week 2 – Personal Study

A Vital Ministry

 **Cross reference: video notes pages 47–48**

Reading: Luke 10:25–37

"But a certain Samaritan, as he journeyed, came where he was: and when he saw him, he had compassion on him." Luke 10:33 (AV)

This week we are exploring how we can develop effective skills for encouragers, but before we look at how, we need to ask the question – Why? Why do we want to be encouragers?

In the book of Corinthians Paul underlines an important and vital issue of ministering with the right motives:

"The Lord ... will bring to light what is hidden in the darkness and will expose _____ of men's hearts." 1 Corinthians 4:5

If we do not consider our motives it is possible to reach out to care for others as an attempt to meet some need within ourselves.

What might be some needs we are trying to meet in ourselves by wanting to help others?

_____

_____

_____

The significance of caring is that its focus is to give and not get, giving of yourself and expecting nothing in return. Often we go through life looking to others to give us "strokes" or "warm fuzzies" – in other words looking for the "feel-good factor" – and so we begin to manipulate relationships for what we can get out of them. We want the attention, approval and affirmation from others to give us the feeling of significance and importance, or sometimes just because of a need to feel wanted and needed.

Read through the following, and tick any motivation you may find in yourself:

❏ I like to flatter others   ❏ I'm fishing for compliments

❏ I want others to like me   ❏ I want others to say nice things about me

❏ To make me feel good   ❏ I need a favour

❏ I enjoy power and control   ❏ It makes me feel significant

❏ I want to be affirmed and   ❏ I can't bear to be criticised
   accepted

What was the key motivation in Christ's life?

       Matthew 9:36
       Matthew 20:34
       Matthew 23:37   _____
       Mark 1:41
       Luke 7:13

How did Paul express it? – 2 Corinthians 5:14

_____

It is important to recognise that in God's purposes what we do is less important than why we do it. If you make a large financial gift to the Church with the goal of impressing others with your generosity, then your actions will go unrewarded.

Philippians 2:3 *"Do nothing out of* _____ *or*

_____*but in humility* _____ *"*

Sometimes if we do not want to face and deal with issues in our own life, we prefer to focus on trying to solve issues in other people's lives. It is as we allow God to deal deeply with the unresolved issues in our own life, that He can effectively use us in helping and caring for others.

A definition of love in the writings of the old American evangelist Charles Finney says this:

"Love is bringing about the highest possible good in another individual's life."

In order to achieve this with the right motive, it is imperative that you recognise how much God loves and cares for you. Remember the old saying – "you can only take a person along life's pathway as far as you have gone yourself". Beyond that point you journey together into unknown territory and uncharted waters. We can only effectively give out of the supply that we have drawn on ourselves:

Read:

1 John 4:8–10
Revelation 1:5
Ephesians 3:17–19
Psalm 139:13 –18

What do these scriptures tell us about God's love for us?

_____

_____

_____

For Action:

Next Sunday, or when appropriate, participate with your group in taking bread and wine and contemplate afresh God's great love for you in sending His Son and the immense price and great sacrifice He made. As you take the bread and wine let His love overwhelm you afresh.

List some of the evidences of God's love for you:

_____

_____

_____

Out of the sense of God's love for you, commit yourself to serving others rather than being served. Caring for others means being willing to have a servant heart, putting the needs of others first.

"Each of you should look not only to your own interests, but also to the interests of others. Your attitude should be the same as that of Christ Jesus: Who, being in very nature God, did not consider equality with God something to be grasped, but made himself nothing, taking the very nature of a servant, being made in human likeness."
Philippians 2:4–7

In what ways did the Samaritan in today's reading display the caring servant heart:

_____

_____

_____

Motivation to care must be out of a heart of love, a willingness to serve, and an overwhelming sense of God's love – recognise that people will not always respond as we expect and that they may even hurt us in the process. Follow the example of Christ, who even in His moments of deepest pain reached out to care for the spiritual well-being of the dying thief.

The Lord Jesus seized even this opportunity to reach out to a hungry heart and needy soul, remember, as we stressed on the video, be alert to the opportunities that may present themselves to you today. Looking out for others does not come naturally – be alert! Prayerfully each day look to the Lord to provide opportunities to come alongside someone. Ask Him to give you alertness, wisdom and discernment to seize the opportunity as it presents itself.

In the video we listed some areas to be alert to – see if you can put some specifics next to them:

Subtle hints: Downcast expressions:

e.g.   Agitated movement_____   e.g.   Furrowed brow_____

       _____   _____

       _____   _____

Uncharacteristic behaviour:

e.g.   Irritability _____

_____

_____

Letting routine tasks go:

e.g.   Not paying bills _____

_____

_____

Indecisiveness:

e.g.   Putting off phone calls _____

_____

_____

Tone of voice:

e.g.   Curt response _____

_____

_____

Change of personal presentation:

e.g.   Not shaving _____

_____

_____

When we spot these signals, the key words to remember are awareness and sensitivity. We might enquire gently "How are you doing today, John?" A common retort is "Not too bad." A good response is "Does that mean not too good then?" Usually the reply gives you the opportunity to begin to explore the possibility of caring by encouragement.

Prayer: **Lord, help me today by Your Spirit to tune into someone who is hurting. Lord, I know my tendency is to focus on myself and my own needs, give me grace today to trust You more in order that I might be an instrument in Your hand to be an encouragement to someone else. Amen.**

Care Practical Application:

_____

_____

_____

Learning to Listen

📺 Cross reference: video notes pages 48–49

📖 Reading: James 1:19 –25

> *"My dear brothers, take note of this: Everyone should be quick to listen, slow to speak and slow to become angry, ..."* James 1:19

The art of listening does not come easily for most of us. Naturally most of us are better talkers than listeners, but we can all learn to listen. Someone has said that God has given us two ears and one mouth because He wants us to listen twice as much as we talk.

Read:

Proverbs 1:5
Proverbs 18:13
James 1:19

What do they say about listening?

_____

_____

_____

A clear indication of your care is felt by your willingness to take time out to listen. Being willing to listen is a clear expression and demonstration of your desire to love. Learning to listen is a discipline each of us needs to practice. The tendency is always to want to speak. Listening is not just hearing, but taking time to understand.

Read:

Proverbs 12:18
Proverbs 13:3
Proverbs 17:27–28
Proverbs 29:20

What do these verses teach us?

_____

_____

_____

Good listening involves a number of elements that were briefly mentioned on the video:

1 Develop a total awareness of the other person

The tendency so often when listening is to drift in and out, because the pressures, responsibilities and activities of our own lives keep pressing in upon our minds. We have all had experiences at one time or another of losing track in a conversation because our minds have wandered. Although our mouths and focus have still been engaged in a conversation, we are only half listening.

The key discipline here is:

undivided attention and total concentration.

2 Not thinking about what you are going to say next

Because we feel we have insight, wisdom and the "right answer" invariably we are more concerned about sharing our answer than we are to listening to and understanding the question. Again our motive comes into question, we often gain a greater sense of our own importance by telling what we know, rather than remaining quiet and not pre-judging what we are going to hear. How can we also listen to what the Lord might be wanting to say, when our minds are full of our own ideas?

The key discipline here is:

don't pre-judge, be willing to lay aside all pre-conceptions.

3 Focus on the feeling that lies beneath the words

Words are often like tell-tale puffs of smoke that signify that there is an emotional volcano lurking beneath ready to erupt. Words are often loaded with emotion, and it is important that we learn to hear the emotion contained in the words – we call this active listening.

Tune in to the following statements and see if you can pick up the feeling that lies buried beneath the words:

1 "My job is all right at the moment but things keep changing. I don't think it will be long, however, before I will be replaced by a machine."

Person is feeling _____

2 "I think my son is on drugs. I can't be sure but he has all the signs of a drug addict."

Person is feeling _____

3 "The date for the wedding has been set but the closer it gets the more I feel like postponing it."

Person is feeling _____

4 "I talked to my pastor about the problem and he said he would arrange to see me to discuss it. That was a month ago and he hasn't come back to me with a date yet."

Person is feeling _____

5 "I lost my temper again today and although I have made a commitment not to do this, it keeps happening. I'm a pretty hopeless Christian."

Person is feeling _____

Always remember that caring and listening to a person's feelings brings you right into the "living room" of their lives.

The key discipline here is:

tuning in and actively listening.

4 Empathise with hurt feelings

Empathy has been described as "your pain in my heart". It is letting someone know that you know and understand how they feel. We call this process reflecting back, or feeding back by restating with fewer words the content and emotions that they have shared with us.

Read Hebrews 4:15 – How can we link empathy with this verse?

_____

_____

_____

What is the difference between empathy, pity and sympathy?

_____

_____

_____

The key discipline here is:

feeding back or reflecting back.

5 Giving non-judgemental acceptance

Often people share things that we may find unacceptable or shocking. At this point we need to guard our immediate reactions of a shock, horror response that stops them dead in their tracks and prevents them from sharing any further. A good listener is one who on first receiving information does not condemn on one hand, but who also does not condone on the other hand. Unless you are able to listen clearly and calmly to all of the facts, then you are not a good listener. You need to transmit two messages by your listening – I am interested in what you say and I will accept you regardless of what you might say. The appropriate time will come when you need to face the facts, but it is not at this stage of listening.

The key discipline here is:

not condoning and not condemning.

Are You a Good Listener?

Think of a meaningful conversation you have had recently and recall it in a sentence or two:

_____

_____

_____

Listening Test

Circle the term that best describes you as a listener:

Superior   Excellent   Good   Above average

Average   Below average   Poor   Terrible

How do you think the following would rate you as a listener? (0–10)

Your best friend   [   ]   Your boss   [   ]
A work colleague   [   ]   A subordinate   [   ]
Your spouse   [   ]

Whenever we are willing to take time out to listen effectively we demonstrate care. When a person begins to feel understood they feel that you have their best interests at heart – you care about them. Take time to listen.

Prayer: **Lord, I seem to be a better talker than a listener. I need to listen to You more to hear Your voice, and I ask for Your help in learning to listen more attentively to those I am seeking to care for and encourage. Amen.**

Care Practical Application:

_____

_____

_____

Optional Exercise

Rate yourself: circle your response on a scale of 1 to 10.

1 More focused on personal thoughts and things occupying the mind

Totally focused on what the other person is saying

1	2	3	4	5		6	7	8	9	10

2 More aware of what is going on around or of external things about the other person

Fully aware of and concentrating on what the other person is saying

1	2	3	4	5		6	7	8	9	10

3 Thinking up my next sentence and forming it in my mind

Being completely open minded as to the response that will need to be made

1	2	3	4	5		6	7	8	9	10

4 Interpreting the facts before I've had time to hear them all

Listening to the facts without putting interpretations upon them

1	2	3	4	5		6	7	8	9	10

5 Listening to the words in a factual way only

Listening for the feelings and observing the body language

1	2	3	4	5		6	7	8	9	10

6 Being insensitive to underlying feelings

Drawing out, exploring and encouraging feelings to be expressed

1	2	3	4	5		6	7	8	9	10

7   Disregarding expressed feelings
    and ignoring them

    1   2   3   4   5

Identifying with hurt feelings and
supporting them

    6   7   8   9   10

8   Giving no indication of understanding
    what is being said

    1   2   3   4   5

Feeding back content and
reflecting the feelings expressed

    6   7   8   9   10

9   Judging content and expressing
    personal views

    1   2   3   4   5

Accepting and evaluating content
at face value

    6   7   8   9   10

10 Showing prejudice by immediately
    responding with the answer

    1   2   3   4   5

Not judging or responding until
the point expressed is understood

    6   7   8   9   10

11 Showing disinterest, impatience, or
    boredom through body language

    1   2   3   4   5

Demonstrating appropriate body
movements that show attention,
concern and interest

    6   7   8   9   10

12 Reacting to unacceptable life
    experiences and negative emotions

    1   2   3   4   5

Showing acceptance and understanding without condoning or
condemning

    6   7   8   9   10

The Awesome Power of Words

 Cross reference: video notes page 50

 Reading: James 3

> *"With the tongue we praise our Lord and Father, and with it we curse men, who have been made in God's likeness. Out of the same mouth come praise and cursing. My brothers, this should not be."* James 3:9–10

To be a good encourager we need to understand the power and effectiveness of words. James, in our reading today, tells us that with the ability of our tongue we are able to bless or curse.

Boys flying kites haul in their white wing birds

But you can't do that when you are flying words.

Thoughts unexpressed may fall back dead

But even God cannot kill words once they're said.

List some words that bless and words that blister:

Bless: e.g. Well done _____   Blister: e.g. Hopeless _____

_____   _____

_____   _____

Read:

Proverbs 10:11 & 20
Proverbs 15:4
Proverbs 18:21

Write a summary sentence:

_____

_____

_____

An encourager must recognise the power of his words and must always seek to use them in such a way that they will build up the other person.

> *"Do not let any unwholesome talk come out of your mouths, but only what is helpful for building others up according to their needs, that it may benefit those who listen."* Ephesians 4:29

Insensitive Statements

List the reasons why the following statements made on the video are insensitive:

"You need more faith"

_____

_____

_____

"Praise the Lord anyway"

_____

_____

_____

"You shouldn't feel like that"

_____

_____

_____

"It might never happen"

_____

_____

_____

Can you think of other insensitive statements that are sometimes made?:

_____

_____

_____

Can you think of an insensitive statement that you have made recently?:

_____

_____

_____

Put together some statements that are:

1 Prompted by love – Proverbs 15:23

> *"A man finds joy in giving an apt reply – and how good is a timely word!"*

e.g. I may not be able to help but I am a good listener and I care. _____

_____

_____

_____

2 Chosen with care – Proverbs 25:11

> *"A word aptly spoken is like apples of gold in settings of silver."*

e.g. I sense you are struggling at the moment. If you need someone to share with I am happy to make the time. _____

_____

_____

_____

3 Spoken with tenderness – Proverbs 12:25

"An anxious heart weighs a man down, but a kind word cheers him up."

e.g. Thanks for sharing that, I know it wasn't easy for you and I sense something of the pain you are feeling. _____

_____

_____

_____

Exercise

Assess the dialogue in the conversation you observed in the video presentation between Bill and John. See how many inappropriate responses you can find, then assess it on a scale of 1–10:

Bill: "Hello, John, how are you today?"

John: "Oh, not so bad really; I've been better."

Bill: "What's wrong, John? Things not going too well at home?"

John: "Well, I'm not sure whether I should really be discussing my problems with anyone at the moment."

Bill: "I know it is sometimes difficult to talk about things related to one's family, but why don't you try telling me your problem and I'll see if I can help you."

John: "Well, it's nothing to do with my family really, although it will affect them in due course. The truth is, I think I'm going to be made redundant."

Bill: "Well, you'll be in good company, John. Remember there are thousands and thousands with a similar problem at the moment."

John: "Yes, I know, and that's what makes me feel worse. I feel so ... er ... selfish I suppose."

Bill: "I think you are being selfish, John. Isn't it great, John, to know the truth of Romans 8:28, that "all things work together for good to those who love God"? In the light of that, you ought to be praising the Lord, John! Say "Praise the Lord".

John: "Praise the Lord"

Bill: "That's better. Doesn't that make you feel differently already?"

John: "I suppose so."

Bill: "You've got to remember, John, that it isn't the end of the world. You might be losing your job, but you mustn't lose your courage. Remember, when the going gets tough, the tough get going. What have you been doing about looking for another job?"

John: "Well, nothing really, I've been so shattered that I haven't been able to think straight."

Bill: "Well, now, snap out of it, John. Things will get better. We all have days when we don't feel like facing up to issues, but you have got to face it for the sake of yourself and your family."

John: "I know."

Bill: "Have you told your wife about this yet?"

John: "Well, no – I don't want to trouble her unnecessarily. It might not happen, after all."

Bill: "Well, I think you should, John. Share it with her when you get home today. Goodbye John. I hope things get better for you. I'm sure they will."

What is the cardinal error that Bill has made?

_____

To use words wisely we must discipline our use of the tongue in order to bring words that bless not blister, heal not hurt, and care not cut, showing sensitivity, love, care and tenderness.

Prayer: **Lord, I commit myself today to choosing words and using words that You can bless to bring richness, grace and strength to those I care for. Amen.**

Care Practical Application:

_____

_____

_____

Developing Your Door Opener Skills

 Cross reference: video notes page 51

Reading: Job 15:1–13, 16:1–5

> *"But my mouth would encourage you; comfort from my lips would bring you relief."* Job 16:5

This is a technique for helping people to share, that ought to be developed and practised by every encourager. They are responses to statements people make that help a person to open their heart and life to us, rather than responses that close the door of opportunity. They provide the possibility for further sharing rather than a premature end to the conversation.

Example:

Statement:	"How on earth was George invited to do that job?"

Door Closers:

1 I've wondered the same myself.
2 That's a good question.
3 He must have connections.

Door Openers:

1 How do you feel about it?
2 Do you not think he's the right person?
3 Sounds like you might have a problem with that?

Exercise:

Statement: "How are things going?" "Oh, not so bad."

Door Closers:

1 _____

2 _____

3 _____

Door Openers:

1 _____

2 _____

3 _____

Statement: "My children just don't understand me."

Door Closers: 1 _____

                    2 _____

                    3 _____

Door Openers: 1 _____

                    2 _____

                    3 _____

Statement: "My job's getting on top of me. I just can't cope anymore."

Door Closers: 1 _____

                    2 _____

                    3 _____

Door Openers: 1 _____

                    2 _____

                    3 _____

What was Job's complaint against his "carers" in today's reading?

_____

_____

_____

What did he feel he needed?

_____

_____

List some door closers from Job chapter 15:

_____

_____

_____

Although a door opener usually takes the form of a question, it needs to be a question that is open ended and invites a response, that is more than a one word response. We call it an open question.

Examples:

Statement:	"He spoke to me as if I was a small child."
Closed:	"Did you feel upset?"
Open:	"How did you feel when that happened?"

Statement:	"I didn't get much out of the sermon today."
Closed:	"Did you expect to?"
Open:	"What were you expecting to get from today's message?"

Statement:	"I really don't care about it anymore."
Closed:	"Is something the matter?"
Open:	"You don't seem your usual self today, what's happened?"

Statement:	"Stop doing that, you little perisher."
Closed:	"Do you always yell at the children?"
Open:	"How do you find it difficult in handling the problems of the children?"

Think of some statements you have heard recently and identify an open and closed question:

Statement: _____

Closed: _____

Open: _____

Statement: _____

Closed: _____

Open: _____

Evaluate the different responses to the following statement and how you would describe them:

"I can't seem to get on top of things. I've been praying but help just doesn't seem to come. I just can't seem to hear from the Lord."

	Open	Closed	Description
1 When you're close to the Lord you can hear Him.	[ ]	[✓]	e.g. Judgemental ___
2 I understand how badly you feel.	[ ]	[ ]	_____
3 What things are you having trouble getting on top of?	[ ]	[ ]	_____
4 Can you remember a time when you did hear from the Lord?	[ ]	[ ]	_____
5 Have you examined your life to see what the blockage is?	[ ]	[ ]	_____
6 What sort of help would you like to receive from the Lord?	[ ]	[ ]	_____

Exercise

When next in conversation with others, try several door closers and door openers so that you can begin to recognise easily the difference, and the opportunities to explore that are lost and those that are opened.

"The purposes of a man's heart are deep waters, but a man of understanding draws them out." Proverbs 20:5

Prayer: I thank You, Lord, that Your door is always open to me, I can come to Your throne of grace at any moment of the day. Help me to always open doors to others, so that they feel they can share their heart with me. Amen.

Care Practical Application:

_____

_____

_____

Sending Out Non-Verbal Messages

Cross reference: video notes page 51

Reading: Luke 22: 54–62

"And he went outside and wept bitterly." Luke 22:62

Have you ever had a conversation with someone who stares at the floor, or won't look at you as you talk to them. Or someone who continually moves from toe to toe and constantly looks at their watch when you are trying to have a meaningful conversation with them. These are described as non-verbal behaviours, that communicate the message "please finish what you are saying, I have got other things to do." Research shows that it is not only what we say that has impact, but the way we convey it. The experts tell us that communication falls into three categories:

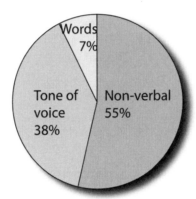

This means that messages we send out can be complimentary or contradictory.

What non-verbal messages do you think Jesus sent to Peter?

_____

_____

_____

How do you think He conveyed it?

_____

_____

_____

What impact did it have on Peter?

_____

_____

_____

List some ways that messages can be complimentary:

Verbal	Tone of Voice	Non-verbal
e.g. That was great	Enthusiastic	Nod of approval
_____	_____	_____
_____	_____	_____
_____	_____	_____

List some ways that messages can be contradicting:

Verbal	Tone of Voice	Non-verbal
e.g. That was great	Sighing	Glare of contempt
_____	_____	_____
_____	_____	_____
_____	_____	_____

We listed five important non-verbal elements on the video, can you think of others?

◆ Focus fully on the person
◆ Respect psychological space
◆ Maintain appropriate posture
◆ Use proper and appropriate eye contact
◆ Match facial expressions

_____

_____

_____

Can you identify some of your own non-verbal ways of communicating?

e.g. Becoming quiet and withdrawn _____

_____

_____

What are some of the ways we can non-verbally communicate our care for others?

e.g. By baking a cake or sending flowers _____

_____

_____

Exercise

Choose three different ways of non-verbal communication you feel comfortable with and express them to three different people within the next 24 hours.

Three Ways   Three People

_____   _____

_____   _____

_____   _____

One of the dangers with encouragement is that we can be drawn in out of our depth. Don't be pressurised into coming up with answers for people, remember you are there to care not cure. The nurse does not carry out the operation on the patient, that is done by a skilful surgeon, but the care and support she gives in tending the patient is crucial to their welfare. Often basic care and understanding gives more encouragement than answers. People don't fall apart because they don't get answers, but because they feel that no one cares.

Put into a sentence what was suggested in the video that you need to do when you come to the extent of your limitations:

_____

_____

_____

Think of someone who you know is struggling at the moment with an issue of life, taking the three words we mentioned in the video on caring prayer, construct a few prayer sentences for them using words under these headings. It's important to recognise that this is a framework and not a formula:

Naturally

_____

_____

_____

Perceptively

_____

_____

_____

Specifically

_____

_____

_____

When you pray, three don'ts:

◆ Don't overwhelm the person with your spirituality

◆ Don't be insensitive to the person's feelings or experiences

◆ Don't pray long rambling prayers

It goes without saying that the carer needs to maintain their own personal prayer life. The caring ministry should always be approached in a prayerful attitude, looking to the Lord for constant wisdom and direction.

The essence of encouraging then is to understand, support and affirm, not to solve, answer, or cure. God alone, the Wonderful Counsellor, is able to meet the deepest needs of the human heart.

Prayer: **Lord, You didn't send a mixed message, You not only declared Your love, but You demonstrated it on the cross. I am eternally grateful. Amen.**

Care Practical Application:

_____

_____

_____

Care Group Review

Spend 50–60 minutes interacting together on the responses you have written down in your own personal study.

Spend about 10–12 minutes for each day with each member of the group having an opportunity to reflect and discuss their responses.

Notes on the Discussion

Day 1

_____

_____

_____

Day 2

_____

_____

_____

Day 3

_____

_____

_____

Day 4

_____

_____

_____

Day 5

_____

_____

_____

Share how you are getting on with your Care Practical Application.

Conclusions for the week:

_____

_____

_____

_____

_____

_____

Programme 3

Caring

The Bible – Our Basis

What is Caring by Exhortation?

In Scripture, the word "exhortation" has a wide meaning but in this seminar it will be used in its most basic sense.

Exhortation is motivating a person to respond to life in accordance with the will of God, as revealed in His Word.

It involves bringing clear direction from the Truth to other people's lives. The most typical way is from the pulpit with the minister addressing the whole congregation. But the process being considered here involves one to one relationships. Caring by exhortation involves one individual coming alongside another in a sensitive way to bring the Word of God to bear on their lives. It is difficult to exhort others if the Word does not take effect in your own life.

"Let the word [spoken by] the Christ, the Messiah, have its home [in your hearts and minds] and dwell in you in [all its] richness, as you teach and admonish and train one another in all insight and intelligence and wisdom [in spiritual things, and sing] psalms and hymns and spiritual songs, making melody to God with [His] grace in your hearts."
Colossians 3:16 (Amplified)

We need to develop a relationship with the Word of God that deeply affects our behaviour.

Why We Need the Ministry of Exhortation

It goes without saying that God would never command us to engage in a ministry that has no point or purpose. If we are to become successful exhorters, then it will be helpful if we consider some of the reasons why this ministry is so necessary.

1   Hurt Feelings Cause People to Lose Perspective Quickly

The story of the prophet Elijah illustrates how intense the hurt feelings can become even for a man of God. 1 Kings 19:3–4

2   Satan Tries to Draw all Christians Away from God

Gradualism is one way in which Satan works. He seeks to draw us away from God without us even realising it.

As values, standards and lifestyles around us change, we become lulled into a false sense that things are normal and acceptable. Because we are constantly exposed to these influences we are in danger of adapting our own lifestyle, attitudes and standards to those around us. This is why we need to be exhorted from the Word of God to prevent Satan gaining a foothold.

3   People Have an Inherently Sinful and Stubborn Nature

In trying to bring about changes in behaviour through the Word of God, we need to understand the strength of the opposition. There's resistance that comes from within our own human nature, as well as influences that come from the society in which we live. All of this causes people to drift from the principles of the Word of God. This is why we need to come alongside people with the ministry of exhortation.

Exhortation needs to take place in the context of a caring relationship.

REMEMBER you cannot

_____ an _____ person

The Basis of Exhortation

Advice and counsel can come from many directions, but good advice is not necessarily God's advice. In fact, Godly wisdom often flies in the face of natural reasoning. We can look in many directions for advice and insight.

So often we tend to look for the help of professionals and experts. Could it be that we often put our trust in what they say more than Scripture. Instead of imposing the experts' views, we need to expose people to the truth of Scripture.

The only safe and reliable foundation on which the ministry of exhortation can be based is the

_____

The Bible is not just a history book, but contains powerful truths which, under the control of the Holy Spirit, help to bring us to spiritual maturity.

An examination of a key verse in Scripture shows how these truths are focused in four specific directions.

"All Scripture is given by inspiration of God, and is profitable for doctrine, for reproof, for correction, for instruction in righteousness." 2 Timothy 3:16 (NKJ)

The Four Phases of the Word of God

Before we can become effective exhorters we must allow the four phases of God's Word, to become a part of our daily lives.

Phase 1: Doctrine The basic elements of our faith.

Violation of the Word

Phase 2: Reproof When we've broken or missed God's principle.

Phase 3: Correction The heart of exhortation – truth that changes lives and behaviour.

Phase 4: Instruction in Righteousness How to maintain God's principles for living.

IN SUMMARY

Caring Through Exhoration

Motivating Biblical responses because:

◆ hurt feelings cause lost perspectives

◆ Satan tries to draw us away from God

◆ we have a sinful and stubborn nature

The basis of exhortation is the Bible

CARE GROUP DISCUSSION

In your small groups review the video using the following questions to stimulate your discussion. They are only guidelines to help you think through what you have viewed.

Remember! The goal here is to review the video material together.

1   **Talk through the concept of exhortation from a traditional viewpoint.**

2   **Discuss its definition in the caring context.**

3   **Think through together the concept of hurt feelings causing a loss of perspective.**

4   **How did you feel about the influence of Satan and the sinful nature.**

5   **Talk through together the concept of the four phases of God's Word.**

6   **Talk through any other aspects of the presentation you have thoughts on.**

Don't worry if you have not covered all the questions.

Programme 3

Caring

The Bible – Our Basis

Week 3 – Personal Study

What is Exhortation?

Cross reference: video notes page 87

Reading: Psalm 119:97–105

> *"How sweet are your words to my taste, sweeter than honey to my mouth!"*
> Psalm 119:103

There are three important elements in the process of Christian Caring. As we have seen, the first and foremost is the significance of encouragement. Always remember, that you cannot effectively exhort an unencouraged person. If we really care for people, we can't leave them there, we need to encourage them to move forward, finding a clear sense of hope concerning God's direction for life. The word the Bible uses for describing this part of the caring process is exhortation. In the New Testament the same Greek word is also used for encouragement. They are the twin concepts that need to flow together; if you like, two sides of the same coin. Following this week's video we now explore further the ministry of caring through exhortation.

Word Study – Paraclete – Paraklesis

a) Encouragement – being called alongside, to bring strength, comfort, support and courage.

   Dictionary definition, "One who puts courage and confidence into someone".

b) Exhortation – to persuade, entreat or invite someone to pursue a particular course of action or conduct; bringing hope and direction for life in the light of grace and truth. To build someone up.

   Dictionary definition, "To urge someone earnestly or to advise someone strongly".

It is quite clear from Scripture that the ministry of exhortation is not just for a gifted few but a ministry for all.

Read:

Romans 12:8
Colossians 3:15,16
1 Thessalonians 2:11,12
1 Thessalonians 5:11

Write out in your own words a summary of the above verses:

_____

_____

_____

Read:

Colossians 1:28.

What are the four goals of caring by exhortation in this verse:

1 _____

2 _____

3 _____

4 _____

Read:

Hebrews 6:17–20.

What does God want to make clear?

_____

What is described as the "anchor for the soul"?

_____

Read:

Psalm 42:5
Psalm 62:5
Psalm 119:74
Psalm 130:5
Romans 15:4

Write a summary statement:

_____

_____

_____

Think of some of the instances in your own life when you have found hope and direction from God's Word:

Home life _____

The relevant Biblical truth: _____

Professional life _____

_____

The relevant Biblical truth: _____

Church life _____

_____

The relevant Biblical truth: _____

Personal life _____

_____

The relevant Biblical truth: _____

Write down what the overall effect has been:

_____

_____

_____

How have you felt when a word of exhortation you received was not accompanied by genuine care, concern and encouragement?

_____

_____

_____

Who do we usually think or assume in church life has the responsibility for exhortation?

_____

Exhortation then is a highly significant and important ministry for each of us to embrace and participate in. It is not a ministry for a gifted few who are specially called but a responsibility of all of us as we seek to care effectively for each other. When we were saved we inherited a whole family and God wants to use each of us in caring for the family by coming alongside each other to bring hope, direction and a fuller understanding of God's will and purpose for life.

Can you think of an instance in your own life when you have been able to come alongside someone to exhort them by bringing hope and direction?

_____

_____

_____

List three instances in Scripture that you can think of where someone is seen exhorting another person:

1 _____ Scripture Reference _____

2 _____ Scripture Reference _____

3 _____ Scripture Reference _____

List three instances from the Gospels where Jesus is seen exhorting someone:

1 _____ Scripture Reference _____

2 _____ Scripture Reference _____

3 _____ Scripture Reference _____

Prayer: Lord, help me to realise that I can be an instrument in Your hand in helping others to find direction, hope and insight from Your eternal body of truth – the Bible.

Care Practical Application:

_____

_____

_____

Hurt Feelings Cause People to Lose Perspective

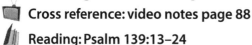 Cross reference: video notes page 88

Reading: Psalm 139:13–24

> *"I praise you because I am fearfully and wonderfully made; your works are wonderful, I know that full well."* Psalm 139:14

In being able to effectively care for people through the ministry of Exhortation it is necessary to understand what may be going on in their lives in order to understand how God might want to speak to them from His Word. But first an important question: Do I allow God to speak into my life? Is the ministry of exhortation operating in my own experience? Do I find hope and direction from God's Word?

In what ways in the last three months have I allowed God to bring direction through exhortation to my life?

Through reading His Word

_____

_____

In prayer/daily quiet time

_____

_____

Through listening to the preached Word

_____

_____

Through conscience

_____

_____

Through reading Christian books

_____

_____

Through spiritual gifts

_____

_____

The Scripture: Our Only Sure and Safe Foundation

A good exhorter is interested not just in the mastering of certain techniques, but in being mastered by certain *convictions*. One of the convictions is that God's Word is trustworthy and reliable.

Write out your definition of a personal conviction:

_____

_____

_____

Important Convictions to Hold

1 The Bible is God's Word written

Jeremiah 36:2
Romans 15:4
1 Corinthians 10:11
Revelation 14:13

Write a summary sentence of the above verses:

I believe _____

_____

_____

2 God's Word speaks to us today

Hebrews 4:12
Psalm 119:9
Ephesians 5:26

Write a summary sentence of the above verses:

I believe _____

_____

_____

3 God's Word contains Life

Psalm 119:103–104
Proverbs 6:23
John 6:63

Write a summary sentence of the above verses:

I believe _____

_____

_____

Optional Exercise

God's Word is eternal

Psalm 119:89
Matthew 5:18
1 Peter 1:25

Write a summary sentence of the above verses:

I believe _____

_____

_____

God's Word is inspired

Acts 1:16
2 Timothy 3:16
2 Peter 1:21

Write a summary sentence of the above verses:

I believe _____

_____

_____

God's Word is applied by the Holy Spirit

John 14:26
John 16:13
1 Corinthians 2:14

Write a summary sentence of the above verses:

I believe _____

_____

_____

God's Word is food for the soul

Deuteronomy 8:3
Jeremiah 15:16
1 Peter 2:2

Write a summary sentence of the above verses:

I believe _____

_____

_____

God's Word is light for the way

> Psalm 119:105
> Psalm 119:130
> 2 Peter 1:19

Write a summary sentence of the above verses:

I believe _____

_____

_____

God's Word is to be written in the heart

> Deuteronomy 11:18
> Psalm 119:11
> Colossians 3:16

Write a summary sentence of the above verses:

I believe _____

_____

_____

It is not enough simply to talk to others about the truth in a detached way, it is important that truth becomes personal to us through its application to our own lives. In this way we are able to truly minister truth to others by the Holy Spirit as we pass it on to them and lovingly draw their attention to it. When we open ourselves more to God's Word we open our hearts more to other people. Truth can then flow through us from heart to heart, not head to head. We not only share God's Word, but ourselves and our relationship with God. People aren't concerned about how much truth you know and can tell them about, but how much you can relate to them in their need with your care and personal understanding and experience of truth.

> *"Let the word of Christ dwell in you richly as you teach and admonish one another with all wisdom, and as you sing psalms, hymns and spiritual songs with gratitude in your hearts to God."* Colossians 3:16

God's Word brings hope when feelings are hurt

"A man's spirit sustains him in sickness, but a crushed spirit who can bear?"
Proverbs 18:14

As people go through different life experiences and are buffeted through difficult circumstances they are often temporarily overwhelmed and lose there sense of direction and purpose. At these times they need clear words to help them refocus and to anchor their souls in the midst of the storm.

Biblical examples of a loss of perspective:
What might have been some of the hurt feelings in these accounts?

Numbers 13:26–14:9 _____

Luke 8:22–25 _____

John 21:1–19 _____

Luke 24:36–43 _____

Can you think of an experience in your own life when hurt feelings caused a loss of hope and direction?

_____

_____

_____

What feelings were present?

_____ _____ _____

_____ _____ _____

Prayer: **Lord, grip me deeply with an abiding conviction of the overwhelming sufficiency of Your Word to meet the deepest needs of the human heart. Amen.**

Care Practical Application:

_____

_____

_____

Satan Constantly Seeks to Draw Us Away From God

 Cross reference: video notes page 88

Reading: Matthew 4:1–11

"Jesus answered, 'It is written: "Man does not live on bread alone, but on every word that comes from the mouth of God." '" Matthew 4:4

The Bible makes it clear that we are in a spiritual struggle and battle. The adversary of our soul seeks to continually ensnare our souls. As carers we are to care and watch out for each other's souls and part of the process of exhortation is helping people to become aware of where Satan may have entangled them in the affairs of this world and to caringly point out the pitfalls along their pathway. Paul exhorts us not to be ignorant of the enemy's devices.

"... in order that Satan might not outwit us. For we are not unaware of his schemes" 2 Corinthians 2:11

Put in a sentence John's warning in 1 John 2:15–17.

_____

_____

_____

The Bible depicts Satan in the following ways:

    An angel of light – 2 Corinthians 11:14
    An adversary – 1 Peter 5:8
    A tempter – 1 Thessalonians 3:5
    A deceiver – 2 Corinthians 11:3
    A hinderer – 1 Thessalonians 2:18
    A Beast – Revelation 19:19
    A roaring lion – 1 Peter 5:8
    The god of this world – 2 Corinthians 4:4
    Prince of the power of the air – Ephesians 2:2
    A liar – John 8:44
    A thief – John 10:10

Satan uses a sixfold strategy to draw us away from God. Under each one give at least one way he seeks to carry it out.

1 Deceives – Genesis 3:13

_____

_____

2 Tempts – Matthew 4:1

_____

_____

3 Spoils – Job 1:9–11

_____

_____

4 Attacks – 1 Peter 5:8

_____

_____

5 Robs – John 10:10

_____

_____

6 Destroys – John 10:10

_____

_____

Can you think of an instance when Satan sought to draw you away from God?

_____

_____

_____

Can you think of an instance when an exhortation from God's Word brought you back on track?

_____

_____

_____

In the reading today (verse 3) how is Satan described?

_____

How did Jesus respond to the three temptations?

_____

"For everything in the world – the cravings of sinful man, the lust of his eyes and the boasting of what he has and does – comes not from the Father but from the world."
1 John 2:16

Often people become ensnared by Satan, because of his subtlety. This was illustrated on the video presentation from the *Screwtape Letters*. It is important for those seeking to develop the ministry of Caring by Exhortation to expose the wiles of Satan for what they are.

Read:

Ephesians 4:26,27

What does Paul point out as one of the wiles of Satan where he seems to gain a foothold?

_____

What might be some other areas of common temptation?

_____   _____   _____

_____   _____   _____

_____   _____   _____

Read:

2 Corinthians 2:10,11

Why does Paul underline the importance of forgiving?

_____

What are we to be aware of?

_____

Read:

2 Corinthians 11:3

What was Paul's concern for the Corinthians?

_____

Read:

Ephesians 6:16

What is the weapon God has given to us in order to withstand the wiles of Satan?

_____

In our walk with God it is important to see Satan in his proper perspective, within the context of Scripture, and not to think of him as more powerful than he really is – neither to regard him as unimportant. He is a personal, aggressive, wicked personality who continually seeks to draw us away from God.

Men don't believe in the devil now, as their
    fathers used to do;
They reject one creed because it's old for another
    because it's new
But who dogs the steps of the toiling saint,
    who spreads the net for his feet,
Who sows the tares in the world's broad fields,
    where the Saviour sows his wheat.
They may say the devil has never lived,
    they may say the devil has gone,
But simple people would like to know –
    WHO CARRIES HIS BUSINESS ON?
                  Anon

Prayer: **Lord Jesus, I thank You that on the cross You defeated Satan the enemy of our souls. Use me, I pray, to help those who have become ensnared by his temptations, through the powerful ministry of Your Word. Amen.**

Care Practical Application:

_____

_____

_____

Our Inherently Sinful And Stubborn Nature

 Cross reference: video notes page 88

 Reading: Galatians 5:13–25

> *"For the sinful nature desires what is contrary to the Spirit, and the Spirit what is contrary to the sinful nature. They are in conflict with each other, so that you do not do what you want."* Galatians 5:17

There is a tendency in every human heart to want to live independently of God. To try and work our lives out the way we think best. To serve our own self interest out of our sense of self sufficiency. Sin in its basic form is living life without depending on and drawing our life from God. People develop all sorts of life patterns in an effort to hold their lives together but without dependency on God at some point it falls apart and ends in tears. Carers who know how to exhort effectively, lovingly, sensitively and firmly draw people back to a new dependency upon Christ and the resources of His Word to undergird their life and walk with Him.

Write out your definition of sin:

_____

_____

_____

Write out the shortest definition of sin repeated five times in Isaiah 14:13–15:

_____ _____ _____ _____ _____

Can you think of some other Biblical references to sinfulness?

_____

_____

_____

When God created us it was in order that we might live out of our relationship with Him. He is the source of life and it was His intention as His created beings that we draw our life from Him. As we have seen, the Fall in the Garden of Eden cut Adam and Eve off from their spiritual source of life. They started to live independently of God and sought to find life by taking control of their own destiny. Ever since the Fall man has been trying to run his life in his own way without reference to God. This is the heart of sinfulness, we have become self-centred individuals.

What are some of the routes down which people go to control their own destiny?

e.g. Achieving success because of the status it brings _____

_____

_____

_____

We have already seen, that God created us as image bearers and that sin has broken and marred God's design for us. One of the things that will help us to become more effective carers is to understand that there is this inbuilt stubbornness within us to try and meet our own needs.

What are some of the ways people selfishly seek to meet their own needs?

e.g. Manipulating and using other people _____

_____

_____

Read:

Jeremiah 17:9
Judges 13:1
Judges 17:6
Proverbs 14:12
Isaiah 55:8

Write a summary sentence of these verses:

_____

_____

_____

Write out in a sentence how sinfulness, stubbornness and selfishness are inextricably linked:

_____

_____

_____

List some characteristics of stubbornness:

_____   _____   _____

_____   _____   _____

List some characteristics of selfishness:

_____   _____   _____

_____   _____   _____

List some characteristics of sinful behaviour:

_____   _____   _____

_____   _____   _____

Can you think of instances when you have struggled with your own stubbornness?

_____

_____

_____

Can you think of instances when you have struggled with your own selfishness?

_____

_____

_____

What sinful behaviour had this led you to?

_____

_____

_____

When parents care for a child and they see them doing things that are not in their best interest, it is out of love that they seek to correct both the attitude and behaviour. It is because of their care that they exhort. The focus of our exhortation is to direct people to God's Word so that changes in attitude and behaviour take place. Take time to understand the three key areas of life's struggle that we have looked at these past three days, and you will have a greater awareness of how the ministry of exhortation directs people to a better way, which is to please the Lord and to draw on the resources of His Word that He has provided for life.

Optional Exercise – Who Meets Your Needs?

Take a moment to examine your own God-dependency. Answer the following questions and give yourself a score between one and five.

1= Poor/No/Negative   5 = Good/Yes/Positive

Read through one at a time	Score 1–5
1 Can I give without demanding anything in return?	
2 Can I support someone without manipulating them?	
3 Do I find my significance in what I do?	
4 Can I disagree with someone without attempting to put them down?	
5 Do I really feel I "belong" to God and that I am unconditionally loved by Him?	
6 How good am I at receiving compliments?	
7 How do I handle my feelings when others ask for my advice and then promptly disregard it?	
8 Am I able to recognise and resist temptation?	
9 How tolerant am I toward others?	
10 How do I rate my sense of worth and value?	
11 How much do I trust other Christians?	
12 How much do I trust God?	
13 Am I easily threatened by others?	
14 Do I always need to be in control?	

	Score 1–5
15 How do I receive criticism?	
16 Do I feel there is a point and a purpose to my existence?	
17 Are my feelings easily hurt?	
18 How well do I relate to others when they are stubborn?	

Prayer: Lord, I can see how so often my sinfulness, selfishnes and stubborn-ness pushes You to the margins of my life. Forgive me, Lord. Thank You for Your loving gentleness in dealing with me, help me to reach out to others in the same way. Amen.

Care Practical Application:

_____

_____

_____

The Basis of Exhortation

 Cross reference: video notes page 89

 Reading: 2 Timothy 3:10–17

> *"All Scripture is God-breathed and is useful for teaching, rebuking, correcting and training in righteousness ..."* 2 Timothy 3:16

Insight and wisdom are essential ingredients in bringing guidance and help to those in need. Human insight and wisdom although at times helpful, is flawed, because it relies solely on the findings of human experience. It comes from the belief that man can find an answer for himself from within himself. This is the basis of humanistic and existential thinking. Man thinks he has the resources to solve his own problems. The solution lies in finding the answer and releasing it from within. All he needs, he tells himself, is his intuition, life experience and his common sense. The Christian perspective is quite the opposite. It recognises that because of sin man is bankrupt and does not have the internal resources to deal with the issues of his own soul. It asserts that the answer lies outside of man – with God, that good advice is not the same as God's advice.

Read:

1 Corinthians 1:25
1 Corinthians 2:14
James 3:13–16

Why is earthly wisdom inadequate?

_____

_____

_____

Read:

Isaiah 55:8–9
Colossians 2:2–3
2 Timothy 3:15
James 1:5
James 3:17–18

Sum up the above verses in a couple of sentences:

_____

_____

_____

Scripture is especially designed to be the basis for caring through exhortation in order to produce spiritual growth and maturity. It focuses on particular processes that are necessary to bring clear direction and stability to our lives. We have described these in the video as the four phases of God's Word and are contained in our reading for today.

1   Doctrine/Teaching – The Principles of Life

"Finally, brothers, we instructed you how to live in order to please God, as in fact you are living. Now we ask you and urge you in the Lord Jesus to do this more and more. For you know what instructions we gave you by the authority of the Lord Jesus."
1 Thessalonians 4:1–2

From Exodus 20:1–17 and Matthew chapters 5–7, list down ten life principles:

1 _____

2 _____

3 _____

4 _____

5 _____

6 _____

7 _____

8 _____

9 _____

10 _____

What are the three most important life principles you have learned from God's Word?

1 _____

2 _____

3 _____

2 Reproof/Rebuking – Showing Us Where Life Principles are Violated

"He who listens to a life-giving rebuke will be at home among the wise."
Proverbs 15:31

Read:

Ephesians 5:3–7
Galatians 5:16–21
1 Peter 2:1

List out ten areas that need reproof from the above passages:

1 _____

2 _____

3 _____

4 _____

5 _____

6 _____

7 _____

8 _____

9 _____

10 _____

Which do you think are the most common?

_____

3   Correction – Showing us How to Put Things Right

"Preach the Word; be prepared in season and out of season; correct, rebuke and encourage – with great patience and careful instruction." 2 Timothy 4:2

Read:

Romans 12:9–21
Galatians 5:22–26
Colossians 3:12–15

List out ten principles of life to restore in people's lives:

1 _____

2 _____

3 _____

4 _____

5 _____

6 _____

7 _____

8 _____

9 _____

10 _____

Which do you think are the most needful?

_____

_____

_____

4 Instruction (or Training) in Righteousness – Showing us How to Continue in Living in Right Relationships.

"And this is my prayer: that your love may abound more and more in knowledge and depth of insight, so that you may be able to discern what is best and may be pure and blameless until the day of Christ, filled with the fruit of righteousness that comes through Jesus Christ – to the glory and praise of God." Philippians 1:9–11

Read:

Matthew 5:6
Romans 14:17
1 Corinthians 1:30
1 Corinthians 13:4–11
1 Timothy 6:11–12
2 Timothy 2:22–25
2 Peter 1:3–9

List ten qualities of righteousness:

1 _____

2 _____

3 _____

4 _____

5 _____

6 _____

7 _____

8 _____

9 _____

10 _____

What was Jesus' new instruction in righteousness? John 13:34

_____

_____

_____

When the four phases of God's Word are applied through the ministry of exhortation the end result is a life of growth and fruitfulness.

> "... so that the man of God may be thoroughly equipped for every good work."
> 2 Timothy 3:17

Prayer: Thank You, Father, for the insight and wisdom contained in Your Word. May I not only allow Your Holy Spirit to operate its four phases, but use me as the instrument to minister them to others. Amen.

Care Practical Application:

_____

_____

_____

Care Group Review

Spend 50–60 minutes interacting together on the responses you have written down in your own personal study.

Spend about 10–12 minutes for each day with each member of the group having an opportunity to reflect and discuss their responses.

Notes on the Discussion

Day 1

_____

_____

_____

Day 2

_____

_____

_____

Day 3

_____

_____

_____

Day 4

_____

_____

_____

Day 5

_____

_____

_____

Share how you are getting on with your Care Practical Application.

Conclusions for the week:

_____

_____

_____

_____

_____

_____

Programme 4

Caring

Applying Biblical Truth – Sensitively

The Focus of Exhortation

The Bible is the basis of our exhortation but we also need to be clear as to what the focus of our exhortation is. The focus is a troubled person.

One of the things that will help us become more effective exhorters is to understand something of what is going on in a person's life, which may be obvious, e.g. bereavement or unemployment, but in others it may be less obvious. Any approach to helping people that focuses on symptoms and ignores the causes is bound to be ineffective. Always remember that:

every person is worth understanding.

Time needs to be taken to understand the person. Sometimes, even with the best of intentions, Scripture can be used in an inappropriate and unhelpful way – driving people to a deeper sense of frustration and despair.

But if we take time to understand the person there are clear advantages:

1   We can Focus on the Root Causes

All behaviour is caused and the causes can often be multiple. Any approach to helping people that focuses on symptoms and ignores the causes is bound to be ineffective.

2   We will see the Person not the Problem as the Focus

Many Christians are problem-orientated rather than person-orientated. That is to say, they see problems when they ought to be seeing people. Remember, behind every human problem is a person.

3   We can be More Confident in Our Approach

Although our dependency should be primarily upon the Holy Spirit, it is true also that spiritual knowledge and understanding help to inspire confidence. A person who has some understanding of how spiritual problems occur will not be at the mercy of circumstances.

Learning to Understand People

It is helpful to see people as having some of the characteristics of an iceberg. The part you can see is above the waterline, but we know that about nine tenths is actually hidden from view. What we see on the surface of people's behaviour should not obscure the fact that beneath the surface there are many thoughts, feelings and attitudes that need to be explored and understood. The Scripture says that: *"out of it [the heart] spring the issues of life."* Proverbs 4:23 (NKJ). Behaviour doesn't just happen, there are always underlying causes.

Please see opposite for the iceberg example.

"... He will not judge by what he sees with his eyes, or decide by what he hears with his ears ..." Isaiah 11:3

1 OBSERVABLE BEHAVIOUR

Water line

2 UNDERLYING CAUSES

Bitterness and resentment

Guilt and shame

Fear and anxiety

3 PRIMARY ISSUE

Choice

Life's problems **OR** **God's promised grace**

Jesus came to be a source of life in all circumstances, not always by changing circumstances, but by changing us from within.

"Be careful that none of you fails to respond to the grace which God gives, for if he does there can very easily spring up in him a bitter spirit which is not only bad in itself but can also poison the lives of many others." Hebrews 12:15 (JB Phillips)

Four Keys to Bring Hope Through Exhortation

Now that we understand the main issue which all Christians face whenever they are engulfed by problems we need to focus on building a Biblical framework which will enable them to remain steadfast and secure no matter what happens. When we take time to understand people we are more able to bring them a sense of hope.

It is useful to group four key ideas which we need to communicate to the people needing hope and exhortation:

1 **God knows everything that happens to us**

2 **God's grace is sufficient for every need**

3 **God brings positive benefits from those circumstances and He turns setbacks into springboards**

4 **God deepens spiritual qualities and characteristics in the process**

"Fearing that we would be dashed against the rocks, they dropped four anchors from the stern and prayed for daylight." Acts 27:29

Often people are looking to God to change their circumstances but when someone can help them to see that God is working in them despite their circumstances, it enables them to draw on His grace and truth to provide the strength they need. The circumstances may not change but they do. This is the deeper character change and dependence on God that He brings about in our lives. God's principal objective is not happiness, that is to make all the circumstances come good again, but *holiness*, that is that we might become more like Jesus in the way we handle all of life's circumstances.

Principles and Skills for Successful and Effective Exhortation

Now that the core element of exhortation has been identified, the next stage is to focus on learning some of the skills and principles that will enable you to make your ministry of exhortation effective.

1 Develop the _____

Caring involves more than engaging in the right actions – it also involves having the right attitudes.

Remember the mistakes made by Job's "comforters", with their:

Superior attitude (Job 15:7–13)
Judgemental attitude (Job 8:1–7)
Superficial attitude (Job 19:13–19)

Although at times they appeared to hit the mark, they nevertheless failed in their attempts to encourage and exhort. Job viewed them as "miserable comforters".

2 Ask _____ and _____ Questions

The power of a perceptive and well-phrased question is a tremendous aid in helping a person see things in perspective.

Perceptive questions have several ingredients. They are:

1 used sensitively
2 clear and appropriate
3 open ended
4 properly paced
5 releasing – encouraging the other person to be open and respond to a genuine interest
6 no sense of direct or implied criticism – they are gentle and non-threatening

3   Recognise the Importance of _____

Being able to say the right thing at the right time.

The Walk to Emmaus – Luke 24:13–32

One of the biggest mistakes is to bring the Word of God too quickly – timing is of the utmost importance. Proverbs 15:23 says: *"Everyone enjoys giving good advice, and how wonderful it is to be able to say the right thing at the right time!"* (TLB)

Jesus came alongside the disciples and gets into step with them

◆ He asked questions, but didn't confront them in a judgemental way. He encourages them to ventilate their hurt and downcast feelings

◆ He listened – allowing them to express themselves, to share their thoughts and feelings

Once He had built a deep and empathetic relationship with them

◆ He exhorted them – He explained the Scriptures that brought perspective and new understanding

He had demonstrated His willingness to listen to them and so they were willing to listen to Him. The result – their hearts burned within them.

Lesson: Don't move too quickly to bring people in touch with the Scriptures. Respect their hurt feelings.

We all have to earn the right to be exhorters and one way we do that is by getting to know all we can about a person's circumstances, thoughts and feelings.

4   Make Sure You are not Drawn into a _____

This is a trap many Christians can fall into when attempting to exhort. The essence of a power struggle is one person trying to change another.

Remember the rich young ruler – Christ gave him the truth and when he chose to resist it Christ allowed him to walk away. A power struggle comes about because of failure to differentiate between two important things – concern and control. You must never make it your goal to change a person. Your goal should be to share with them all you feel the Lord wants you to share and allow the Holy Spirit to bring about the change.

The best way to help someone struggling with resistance to truth is:

1   Share gently what you feel is going on

2   Acknowledge again the circumstances of their life and situation

3   Sensitively and lovingly restate the truth

Remember, sanctification (ongoing Christian growth) is a continuing process.

IN SUMMARY

Exhortation is:

Motivating people to Biblical responses

Understand what's going on beneath
the waterline

Develop appropriate skills:

    right attitudes
    right questions
    right timing
    avoid a power struggle

Follow Christ's example

CARE GROUP DISCUSSION

In your small groups review the video using the following questions and comments to stimulate your discussion. They are only guidelines to help you think through what you have viewed.

Remember! The goal here is to review the video material together.

1 **Is everyone worth understanding? – Discuss.**

2 **Talk through the advantages suggested when we do take time to understand people.**

3 **Review the idea of observable behaviour being linked to underlying causes.**

4 **What did you feel about the primary issue in learning to understand people?**

5 **Talk through the four keys that bring hope.**

6 **Review the different skills that were suggested.**

7 **Think through together the problem of the power struggle.**

Don't worry if you have not covered all the questions.

Programme 4

Caring

Applying Biblical Truth – Sensitively

Week 4 – Personal Study

Learning to Understand People

📺 Cross reference: video notes pages 125–126

📖 Reading: Hebrews 4:12–16

"For the word of God is living and active. Sharper than any double-edged sword, it penetrates even to dividing soul and spirit, joints and marrow; it judges the thoughts and attitudes of the heart." Hebrews 4:12

We must always remember that exhortation does not focus on our ability to handle Scripture or even on the fact that someone may be struggling with a problem, it focuses on the person themselves. They are not a problem and must not be viewed as such, they may have a problem but are a person to be loved. Taking time to understand a person, is far more important than imposing the "right answers" on them. People are much more willing to listen to us if they feel that we have taken the time to understand what is going on in their life. People do not care how much you know, they want to know how much you care. Taking time to find out about people has three major benefits.

1   **It enables us to understand root causes**

   "He will not judge by what he sees with his eyes, or decide by what he hears with his ears;" Isaiah 11:3

   TAKE TIME TO EXPLORE AND UNDERSTAND

2   **Focus on the person not the problem**

   "Unto him that loved us and washed us from our sins in his own blood." Revelation 1:5 (AV)

   PEOPLE ARE NOT PROBLEMS, THEY HAVE PROBLEMS

3   **It helps you to be more confident in your approach**

   "For we do not have a high priest who is unable to sympathise with our weaknesses, but we have one who has been tempted in every way, just as we are – yet without sin." Hebrews 4:15

   EVERY PERSON IS WORTH UNDERSTANDING

Respond to this statement with several answers learned from your observation of others and your life experience.

People behave the way they do because:

1 _____

2 _____

3 _____

We saw in the video that people have feelings and often operate from that level. God created us with feelings, He feels and He created us in His image. We know that the image is marred due to the damage of sin and so we experience emotions which work against us. We describe these as negative emotions which if left unaddressed become unhelpful and unhealthy, eventually becoming debilitating, incapacitating and sometimes, paralysing. When we begin to look at the world of emotions, we find that when the Fall took place, three dominant "Families" of emotions emerged.

Read:

Genesis 2:25
Genesis 3–4:6

Pick out the dominant emotions.

_____

_____

_____

As soon as the personality disintegrated because of sin these strong emotions emerged and affected behaviour patterns. We describe these emotions as "signal emotions", just like a red light on the dashboard that warns us that something is wrong and needs to be put immediately right. These signal emotions are God's warning system, telling us something is wrong in the personality. Taking time to understand what these signals mean and how to address them is an extremely important part of the ministry of exhortation and a demonstration of true caring.

Guilt and Shame

Guilt and shame arise from a sense of personal failure. The Greek word for sin is HAMARTIA – which means missing the mark or failing to attain to the standard, especially in relation to love.

What are some other emotions that belong in this family?

e.g. Self contempt _____   _____   _____

What are some of the things people often feel guilty about?

1 _____

2 _____

Think of some of the ways people try to compensate for their guilt and shame in their behaviour patterns.

1 _____

2 _____

What life attitudes emerge from guilt and shame?

e.g. Inferiority _____   _____   _____

Think of at least three Biblical characters who failed and were restored.

_____   _____   _____

What makes you feel guilty and ashamed?

_____

_____

What is God's antidote for guilt and shame?

1 John 1:9 _____

Romans 8:1 _____

Fear and Anxiety

Fear and anxiety come from a sense of uncertainty in the personality, on not being sure what the outcome will be. The Greek word PHOBOS means dread or terror, of being scared and wanting to run away, because of possible consequences.

What are some of the things that people are often afraid of or anxious about?

1 _____

2 _____

What are some other emotions that belong to this family?

e.g. Apprehension _____ _____

Think of some of the ways people handle their fear and anxiety through their life patterns.

1 _____

2 _____

What life attitudes emerge from fear and anxiety?

e.g. Withdrawn _____ _____

Think of three Bible characters who were afraid?

_____ _____ _____

What makes you feel fearful and anxious?

_____

What is God's antidote for fear and anxiety?

1 John 4:18 _____

Philippians 4:6–7 _____

Bitterness and Resentment (Anger)

Bitterness and resentment come from being angry that things have not turned out the way we wanted them to according to our plans and self interest. Self focus and self centredness is at the heart of bitterness and resentment. The Greek word ORGE for anger means inward indignation and PIKRIA for bitterness means unrelenting, cutting or sharp reaction of the soul.

What are some of the things that people often get bitter and resentful about?

1 _____

2 _____

What are some of the emotions that belong to this family?

e.g. Hostility_____   _____   _____

What are some of the ways people handle their bitterness and resentment?

1 _____

2 _____

What life attitudes emerge from bitterness and resentment?

e.g. Self protection_____   _____   _____

Think of three Bible characters who were bitter and resentful:

_____   _____   _____

What makes you bitter and resentful (angry)?

_____

_____

What is God's antidote for bitterness and resentment?

Hebrews 12:5_____

Proverbs 19:11_____

We all experience these emotions as part of life, but as we learn to recognise them, and the life patterns that follow, we have a choice to either embrace them and their consequences or to respond to Grace and Truth which frees us from them and transforms us into His likeness.

We have seen his _____ full of_____ and _____
John 1:14

He has called us to be _____
Romans 8:29

Prayer: **Thank You Lord that the Bible is an honest book, and that even some of Your choice servants did not always get it right. I am so grateful that You have made a way back from guilt, fear and anger through forgiveness received at the foot of the cross. Amen.**

Care Practical Application:

_____

_____

_____

Keys to Bring Hope

 Cross reference: video notes page 128

Reading: Romans 15:1–13

> *"May the God of hope fill you with all joy and peace as you trust in him, so that you may overflow with hope by the power of the Holy Spirit."* Romans 15:13

Having considered the underlying emotions that people struggle with we need to seek to help to build a framework that will encourage them to live the way God has planned for them. It does not mean that all issues and difficulties will dissolve. It is in midst of these difficulties that a good exhorter is able to bring hope and direction. This is the essence of Exhortation.

What is the main concern which arises in the heart of someone who is faced with a deep and pressing problem?

Do I give way to _____ or is there _____

1 God Knows Everything that Happens to Us

Fill in the appropriate phrase from each verse.

Matthew 10:29–31 _____

Romans 8:28 _____

Philippians 1:6 _____

1 Thessalonians 5:24 _____

Hebrews 12:2 _____

Write a summary sentence you could share with someone else.

_____

_____

_____

Optional Exercise

Write down a circumstance when you couldn't see God in it.

_____

_____

_____

_____

How did you feel?

_____

_____

_____

When you look back what do you think now?

_____

_____

_____

How might it have helped if someone had caringly shared this concept with you?

_____

_____

_____

2 God's Grace is Sufficient for Every Need

Write down your definition of

Grace

_____

_____

Sufficient

_____

_____

Fill in the appropriate phrase from the following verses:

Romans 5:17 _____

2 Corinthians 12:9 _____

Philippians 4:19 _____

2 Timothy 2:1 _____

Hebrews 4:16 _____

Write a summary sentence you could share with someone else.

_____

_____

_____

_____

Optional Exercise

Write down a particular instance when you needed God's grace.

_____

_____

What were your thoughts and feelings?

_____

_____

Looking back, how would you describe God's grace to you at that time?

_____

_____

_____

When caring for someone, how do you see yourself being a tangible expression of God's grace?

_____

_____

_____

3 God Turns Setbacks into Springboards

Read:

Genesis 37:12–28
Genesis 45:4–8.

In these passages how did a setback turn into a springboard?

_____

_____

_____

Read:

Acts 16:16–34

In this passage how did God turn a setback into a springboard?

_____

_____

_____

Can you think of another account in the Bible when a setback became a spring-board?

_____

What was the setback of all time that became the springboard of History?
Acts 2:22–36.

_____

How did Peter sum it up?

_____

_____

Write a summary sentence you could share with someone else.

_____

_____

Can you think of an instance in your own life when a setback was turned into a springboard?

_____

_____

_____

4   God Deepens Spiritual Qualities and Characteristics

Fill in the appropriate phrase from the following verses:

Romans 5:3–5   _____

Romans 12:12   _____

Philippians 4:11–13   _____

James 1:2–4   _____

1 Peter 1:6–7   _____

Write a summary sentence you could share with someone else.

_____

_____

_____

Optional Exercise

What circumstances might God allow in order to deepen these qualities in our lives?

Qualities	Circumstances
Love	e.g. Someone unlovable _____
Joy	_____
Peace	_____
Compassion	_____
Faith	_____
Servanthood	_____
Forgiveness	_____
Patience	_____
Trust	_____
Humility	_____

Although we cannot promise to change people's circumstances, we can through the ministry of exhortation bring them fresh hope through these four anchors of truth as we allow the Holy Spirit to use us as ministers of His truth.

Prayer: **Lord help me to fully grasp these Biblical keys of hope and not only implement them in my own life, but to minister them to those who have lost all sense of hope. Amen.**

Care Practical Application:

_____

_____

_____

Principles and Skills 1

📺 **Cross reference: video notes page 129**

📖 **Reading: Job 8:1–7; 15:7–13; 19:13–19.**

"My kinsmen have gone away; my friends have forgotten me." Job 19:14

Develop Right Attitudes

Caring must come out of a relationship not a role. Unfortunately in the passages today Job did not feel that sense of caring relationship even though at times the "exhortation" of his "comforters" were fairly close to the truth. How did he describe them?

Job 16:2 _____

In the video presentation we noted 3 wrong attitudes that they displayed from the above passages.

1 Superior

This means talking down to people, making them feel insignificant. List ways that the superior attitude might show itself.

1 _____

2 _____

3 _____

From Job 15:7–13 write down the superior statements.

_____

_____

_____

2 Judgemental

This is prejudging and condemning someone based on our own prejudices. List ways in which the judgmental attitude shows itself.

1 _____

2 _____

3 _____

From Job 8:1–7 list the judgmental statements.

_____

_____

_____

3 Superficial

This means jumping quickly to conclusions, skimming and glossing over the surface. List ways in which the superficial attitude shows itself.

1 _____

2 _____

3 _____

From Job 5:17–27 list the superficial statements.

_____

_____

_____

Clearly these so called comforters lacked any wisdom. Wisdom is the ability to understand a situation and to effectively apply the appropriate knowledge sensitively and discerningly. As exhorters we need wisdom to show the right attitude.

What is Wisdom? The Righteous Application of Knowledge

James says *"If any of you lack wisdom, let him ask of God, that giveth to all men liberally".* James 1:5 (AV). Every exhorter needs wisdom.

According to Colossians 1:9 wisdom is "seeing life from God's point of view" (JB Phillips).

Eight Attributes to Divine Wisdom:

James 3:17 (AV)

(i) _____

Is there any underlying motive for personal fulfilment from manipulating or dominating people? If so, judgement will be impaired through impure motives.

(ii) _____

Right answers are not enough. A caring exhorter must have the right attitude. He needs to experience, first-hand, the peace of God, in order that the troubled may find confidence in his presence.

"Peace I leave with you, my peace I give unto you: not as the world giveth, give I unto you. Let not your heart be troubled, neither let it be afraid." John 14:27 (AV)

(iii) _____

This is one of the most vital characteristics in an effective exhorter. God will never use a counsellor who is rude, rough or harsh.

"And the servant of the Lord must not strive; but be gentle unto all men ..."
2 Timothy 2:24 (AV).

(iv) _____

The caring exhorter needs to be approachable and able to identify with individuals seeking his spiritual help and advice.

(v) _____

The caring exhorter, although he cannot condone sin, must not condemn. He must have a real love and deep concern for the sinner.

"For He gives us comfort in our trials so that we in turn may be able to give the same sort of comfort (strong sympathy) to others in theirs." 2 Corinthians 1:4 (JB Phillips)

(vi) _____

A caring exhorter does not merely tell people what to do, he goes further and helps them to do it.

(vii)_____

The Wisdom which comes from God enables the caring exhorter to remain impartial in his attitudes. Good counselling involves consideration for all who are concerned in any given situation.

(viii)_____

"... that we may bring every man up to his full maturity in Christ." Colossians 1:28 (JB Phillips)

The caring exhorter should follow the principles which he himself gives to others.

The Psalmist describes the right approach in Psalm 55:13–14.

A man like myself – not superior but _____

My companion – not judging but _____

Sweet counsel – not superficial but _____

Prayer: Father, Your Word says that if any man lacks wisdom he can ask You
and You will give him a liberal supply. Grant me Your wisdom as I seek
to reach others through the ministry of exhortation. Amen.

Care Practical Application:

_____

_____

_____

Thoughtful and Perceptive Questions

 Cross reference: video notes page 129

 Reading: Proverbs 18:1–21

> *"The heart of the discerning acquires knowledge; the ears of the wise seek it out."*
> Proverbs 18:15

Questions can either be facilitating or threatening. They can make us feel relaxed or tense. They can put us on our guard or they can encourage a response.

They need to be:

1 Asked sensitively

This means that they are asked gently and in a non-threatening manner: recognising that when using Why? as part of the question it invariably feels threatening but by using How? it is mostly non-threatening. The tone of voice and manner in which questions are asked can also convey insensitivity. We need a gentle manner and a gentle voice.

Try and identify threatening questions:

e.g. Why did you do that?

e.g. Why don't you do your homework?

Why _____

Why _____

Why _____

Try and identify non-threatening questions:

e.g. How do you get on at work?

e.g. How does that seem to be affecting you at the moment?

How _____

How _____

How _____

When we feel we are being asked questions in a threatening way we become defensive and either clam up or become hostile.

2 Clear and appropriate

It is important to learn to ask appropriate questions not inappropriate ones. What would be appropriate areas of life to ask about?

Appropriate areas:

e.g. <u>routine responsibilities</u>

e.g. <u>spiritual life</u>

_____

_____

_____

Think of appropriate questions.

e.g. <u>Can you tell me a little more about the situation?</u>

_____

_____

_____

_____

_____

_____

What would be inappropriate areas of life to ask about?

Inappropriate areas:

e.g. Financial status

e.g. Sexual performance

_____

_____

_____

3 Open-ended

This is learning to phrase your questions in such a way that they cannot be answered by a simple "Yes" or "No".

Exercise with closed and open-ended questions:

Closed	Open-Ended
1 Did you feel upset	e.g. How did you feel when that happened?
2 What's the matter with you today?	e.g. You don't seem your usual self today, how are things?
3 Do you always shout at the children?	e.g. How well do you handle things with the children. Can you give me an example?
4 Do you get along with your husband?	_____
5 I bet you felt depressed about that?	_____
6 That was a stupid thing to say, wasn't it?	_____

4 Properly paced

People need time to think when responding, it is not a game of 20 questions that are rattled off in quick succession. The pace needs to be conversational and attentive with nods and pauses and facial encouragement.

Read through Mark chapters 8–10 and look at the questions Jesus asked and the way He paced the different types of questions. How many of each of the following can you find Him asking?

How _____ Are you _____ What _____

Do you _____ Who _____ Can you _____

Was it _____ Whose _____ Have you not _____

Did you find any others?

_____   _____   _____

Jesus asked why _____ times, but usually in response to a negative, aggressive, hostile questioning approach, not usually to initiate an informed response.

5 Releasing rather than directing

The best place to see this in action is in a court of law. The lawyer must draw information from the witness and not lead the witness or direct them. It is drawing them on to give further information rather than putting words in their mouth.

Complete the following exercise:

Releasing	Directing
Can you tell me a little more ...	e.g. Just do what God asks
Can you enlarge a little further ...	e.g. Just don't do that anymore
What about ...	_____
Help me understand ...	_____

Tell me how that affected you ... Can you explain some more for me ...	_____ _____
Learn to give appropriate responses.	

Evaluate	–	e.g.	That was a wise thing to do.
Interpretive	–	e.g.	It seems you are too dependent on your mother.
Supportive	–	e.g.	Others have felt that way too.
Probing	–	e.g.	Now tell me about ...
Understanding	–	e.g.	I can see it has been pretty hard for you.

Asking questions is a developed skill and needs to be done implementing the principles of these guidelines. We cannot effectively exhort unexplained and unexposed issues. However, for many people exposure is scary and painful, and the underlying concept of building a warm and caring relationship as part of the process in using questions cannot be overemphasised. You can win an argument and lose a friend. You can mishandle questions and lose the opportunity of gently exposing someone to the truth of God's Word that can alone change and meet the deepest needs of the human heart. Your use of questions is the gateway to the heart. Open the gate carefully, gently and sensitively.

Prayer: **Lord, I recognise the importance of good and appropriate questions, give me sensitivity and discernment so that I might be a help and not a hindrance in the helping process. Amen.**

Care Practical Application:

_____

_____

_____

The Importance of Timing

 Cross reference: video notes pages 130–131

 Reading: Luke 24:13–33.

> *"He asked them, 'What are you discussing together as you walk along?' They stood still, their faces downcast."* Luke 24:17

Being sensitive to saying the right thing at the right time is often a significant key in whether we are being helpful or unhelpful. Although we may not sometimes realise it, God is a God of timing. This is borne out in Galatians 4:4:

> *"But when the time had fully come, God sent his Son, born of a woman, born under law ..."*

A big mistake we can make is to give what we think is helpful information too soon. When people's emotions are upset and their minds jumbled, it is difficult for them to hear what we are saying and to respond to it in the way maybe we feel they should. Allow time for them to express their upset emotions and mixed up thoughts. Many of us because we are used to giving advice, enjoy doing it and sometimes it is more important to us, because of the good feeling we get out of it, simply to off-load our advice on others. Take time to explore and understand.

Can you think of an instance in your own life when someone said:

1 Something at the right time that was helpful

_____

_____

How did you feel?

_____

_____

How did you respond?

_____

_____

2 **Something at the wrong time that was unhelpful**

_____

_____

_____

How did you feel?

_____

_____

How did you respond?

_____

_____

In the video presentation we underlined that it is important to explore three significant areas.

1 The Person's Circumstances

It is easy to take for granted that we know certain things but the rule is, never assume that you know something until you hear the person say it to you. A good way to start is to say something like, "John, tell me something of what is going on in your circumstances at the moment". Then allow time for him to tell the story at his own pace.

What are some circumstances that could be explored:

e.g. Work _____   _____   _____

e.g. Family _____   _____   _____

e.g. Church _____   _____   _____

Even if you do know some of these things already, encourage the person to express them from their point of view. Always remember the old adage, a burden shared is a burden halved. Just giving them the opportunity to express their circumstances to someone else who listens and cares is a help in itself. Don't rush them, give them time.

In the encounter with the disciples on the Emmaus road, Jesus illustrates this:

"He asked them, 'What are you discussing together as you walk along?' They stood still, their faces downcast. One of them, named Cleopas, asked him, 'Are you only a visitor to Jerusalem and do not know the things that have happened there in these days?' 'What things?' he asked. 'About Jesus of Nazareth,' they replied. ...." Luke 24:17–19a

Do you think Jesus did not know, of course He did, but He encouraged them to express their circumstances and to talk it out with Him because it was good for them. Jesus slowed His pace to where they were. Remember, others are not where we are, we need to learn to adjust to where they are.

2   Explore How the Person is Feeling

This must be done very gently and slowly as feelings can be very raw and sensitive. The key word to implement here is:

EMPATHY

This means the ability to put yourself into someone else's shoes. We have described it earlier as "your pain in my heart".

Depending on the circumstances, you may be dealing with some initial feelings of shock, fear, worry, hurt. Remember that as you explore this area, feelings can change and may get stronger or may subside.

Example:

Tony comes to see you, he seems agitated and anxious, and as you explore his circumstances you discover that he has just been made redundant. He has a wife and three small children, and feels that his chances of getting another job at his age of 45 are slim, as the local firm where he has always worked is now closing down.

What emotions might be going on in Tony?

e.g. Anxiety _____   _____   _____

_____   _____   _____

_____   _____   _____

Can you think of how you might sensitively bring these feelings to the surface? Construct an appropriate sentence.

_____

_____

_____

Jot down some ways you might empathise.

e.g. Tony if I were you, I know that I would be feeling pretty devastated too _____

_____

_____

_____

3 Exploring a Person's Thoughts

Very often when someone is struggling with some circumstance in life, there is a large element of confusion. They get locked in to their thought processes that whirl endlessly around in their mind, not making sense of the situation. We need to take time to draw these out so that at the appropriate moment we can put them into our Biblical framework of understanding. The danger here is that we want so often to impose our thoughts without taking time to draw out their thoughts.

What might be some of the thoughts going on in Tony's mind?

_____

_____

_____

What sort of statements might you use to draw them out?

e.g. Tell me Tony what is concerning you most at the moment? _____

_____

_____

Remember most exhorters want to give advice and give it now, as soon as they hear information about circumstances, feelings and thoughts they are ready with an answer. The caring exhorter recognises the need to carefully explore and the importance of responding appropriately at the right time. He takes to heart Proverbs 18:13:

"He who answers before listening – that is his folly and shame."

Learn to walk with people through the valley of trouble and give them hope.

"There I will give back her vineyards to her, and transform her Valley of Troubles into a Door of Hope. She will respond to me there, singing with joy as in days long ago in her youth, after I had freed her from captivity in Egypt." Hosea 2:15 (TLB)

4   Avoid a Power Struggle

Because exhortation is drawing a person's attention to truth, it is possible that at the end of the day, they do not want to receive or respond to the truth. Recognise that there may be reasons for that:

◆ **It may be too challenging**
◆ **They may not fully understand it**
◆ **They may need time to think it through**
◆ **They may want to consider its further implications.**

The essence of a power struggle, is a person wanting to impose their will on another and the other resisting. In the video notes we pointed out that we must differentiate between two things:

_____ and _____

Check your own motives:

	Yes	Sometimes	No
Do I want to be in control?	❏	❏	❏
Do I want to be proved right?	❏	❏	❏
Do I want to be seen as the fount of all wisdom?	❏	❏	❏
Do I want to impress?	❏	❏	❏
Do I want to win approval?	❏	❏	❏
Do I want to be seen as being spiritual?	❏	❏	❏
Do I want to expose another's weakness?	❏	❏	❏
Do I want to impose my will?	❏	❏	❏

In Mark 10:17–26 we see Jesus avoiding a power struggle with whom?

_____

Even the most spiritual of people sometimes find it difficult to accept God's solutions for their problems and are resistant to receiving His truth.

Resistance can take two forms:

Reasonable   This is not a rejection of the truth but a questioning and clarifying rather than an immediate response or acceptance. It is usually based on ignorance or lack of understanding and is therefore understandable.

Unreasonable   This is an unwillingness to accept the truth and a clear decision to reject it and rebel against it.

Some ways resistance reveals itself:

◆ **Insincere agreement** – Immediate acceptance in order to please you.
◆ **Excessive emotion** – Using tears to evade the real issue.
◆ **Irrelevant arguments** – The subject doesn't relate to the issue at hand.
◆ **Objection hopping** – Raising one objection after another.
◆ **Sullen quiet response** – A childish ploy to get their own way.
◆ **Direct antagonism** – A hostile and abusive response.

We mentioned three things in the video to help someone struggling with resisting the truth.

1 Share gently what you feel is going on

This means sensitively pointing out that the person is resisting the truth that you are bringing and identifying to them how they are resisting.

From the previous page select two of the ways resistance reveals itself and write down how you would reflect them to someone.

1 _____

_____

2 _____

_____

2 Acknowledge again their circumstances

This is letting them know that you understand what is going on in their life and that this is a very challenging moment for them.

What might you say?

_____

_____

_____

3 Sensitively and lovingly restate the truth

This is sharing with them that although it is extremely challenging, you don't know any other way to resolve the situation other than God's way.

How might you put this to them?

_____

_____

_____

Always remember, that it is the role of the caring exhorter to gently and lovingly expose a person to the truth of God's Word. It is the ministry of the Holy Spirit to bring conviction and not the work of the exhorter to apply pressure that forces a change. Learn to put your confidence and trust in the person and work of the Holy Spirit.

Prayer: Father, your sense of timing is always perfect. You are never too late and never too early. Help me to be sensitive to the timing of the work that you are wanting to do in people's lives. Forgive me for so often rushing in, and grant me grace and patience. Amen.

Care Practical Application:

_____

_____

_____

Care Group Review

Spend 50–60 minutes interacting together on the responses you have written down in your own personal study.

Spend about 10–12 minutes for each day with each member of the group having an opportunity to reflect and discuss their responses.

Notes on the Discussion

Day 1

_____

_____

_____

Day 2

_____

_____

_____

Day 3

_____

_____

_____

Day 4

_____

_____

_____

Day 5

_____

_____

_____

Share how you are getting on with your Care Practical Application.

Conclusions for the week:

_____

_____

_____

_____

_____

_____

Caring

Triggering A Change

What's On Your Mind?

The Ministry of Enlightenment – The Process of How to Change Thinking

We are not so free or independent in our thinking as we might like to think. Every culture makes an indelible impression on its people. The moulding process that begins at birth continues thereafter so that every person is a product of the society in which they live. The human mind is not free even at birth – our minds have been spiritually hi-jacked. The Bible puts it strongly – we are born in sin and shaped in iniquity.

Nevertheless we are thinking beings. The ministry of enlightenment will only be successful if we encourage first, then exhort, and then enlighten.

People can give you their attention with their faces and with their body language but their minds can be thinking about something completely different. Before we can really move into effective Christian living, we must know how to deal with the thoughts that buzz in and out of our heads.

◆ **Football**

◆ **What are we going to eat?**

◆ **How am I going to get through tomorrow at work?**

◆ **I'm missing my favourite television programme**

◆ **When's this guy going to finish?**

◆ **Lunch went on too early – it's probably burning**

The Mind – A Biblical Perspective

Only the Bible can give us a true picture of the human mind. The words, "think", "thought" and "mind" are used more than 300 times in Scripture. There can be no doubt that God views the mind as an important part of human functioning.

"For as he thinks in his heart, so is he." Proverbs 23:7 (NKJ)

Four Biblical Facts Concerning the Mind

1 God has made us with the ability to _____

"Come now and let us reason together ..." Isaiah 1:18 (NKJ)

2 The very first sin arose out of a wrong _____

"... as the serpent deceived Eve by his craftiness, so your minds may be corrupted from the simplicity that is in Christ." 2 Corinthians 11:3 (NKJ)

3 Our _____ have been greatly affected by the Fall

"... whose minds the god of this age has blinded, who do not believe ..." 2 Corinthians 4:4 (NKJ)

4 To function effectively our minds must be _____

"... do not be conformed to this world, but be transformed by the renewing of your mind ..." Romans 12:2 (NKJ)

Do You Hear What You Are Thinking?

One of the things we need to understand if we are to engage in the ministry of Enlightenment is the power and importance of Self-talk. Let's examine some of the features of this strange phenomenon.

1 We talk to ourselves

Though largely unnoticed, we talk continually to ourselves in sentences. And from our inner conversations come our feelings, our reactions, and to some extent – our behaviour.

2 Words flow through our minds at an amazing speed

Those who have studied the phenomenon of Self-talk tell us that we can talk to ourselves at the rate of 1,300 words a minute.

3 Thoughts are unprompted

Sentences can jump into our consciousness without any planning or conscious prompting, and are the result of powerful past influences, events and situations.

4 Some thoughts play repeatedly like tapes

Some thoughts have a way of repeating themselves over and over again – they drone on just beneath the level of consciousness like a tape in a tape recorder. And without realising it, we can be greatly influenced by the messages that are played in our inner audio system.

Independent Thinking is Foolish Thinking

The things that bring us to the edge of depression and bring problems and break-downs are usually the things we are telling ourselves (i.e. the tapes we are playing over and over) because the rest of the personality responds to what we are telling ourselves. If what we are telling ourselves does not include the truth about God, then that thinking leads nowhere, and life goes wrong.

Satan has a profound influence on these tapes. Due to Adam and Eve's capitulation in the Garden of Eden, Satan now has a tremendous vantage point in the human mind. And one of his major strategies is to push us into thinking independently of God. Unless this type of thinking is challenged and corrected, the future has no hope.

Consider this important text:

"Foolishness is bound up in the heart of a child ..." Proverbs 22:15 (NKJ)

The key word in Proverbs is wisdom. God wants to drive out foolish thinking and replace it with wisdom.

As we have seen, we begin life with the propensity to think "foolishly", and unless something dramatic happens to bring about changed attitudes within us, we soon become professional "foolish" thinkers.

Consider the eight stages through which a person passes on the way from birth to eternity:

1 _____ Foolishness

2 _____ Foolishness

3 _____ Foolishness

4 _____ Foolishness

5 _____ Foolishness

6 _____ Foolishness

7 _____ Foolishness

8 _____ Foolishness

God made your mind for Him to think in and if He's not thinking in it, somebody else is. The process of having our thinking changed because God is living in our minds is the process of enlightenment.

Enlightenment – What Is It?

Although the word "enlighten" or "enlightened" is found only a few times in Scripture, it is clear that the need for changed thinking is a key concept in the Word of God:

"Now your attitudes and thoughts must all be constantly changing for the better" Ephesians 4:23 (TLB). The Bible is the only way to deal effectively with the mind. The Word brings the power to change.

The ministry of enlightenment is coming alongside a fellow Christian to assist them in bringing their thinking in line with God's thinking.

It is summarised in Paul's prayer for the Ephesian Christians:

"... the eyes of your understanding being enlightened; that you may know what is the hope of His calling, what are the riches of the glory of His inheritance in the saints, and what is the exceeding greatness of His power towards us who believe, according to the working of His mighty power ..." Ephesians 1:18–19 (NKJ)

The Three Elements Necessary for Effective Enlightenment are:

1 Seeing the _____ from God's point of view:

"that you may know what is the hope of his calling ..."

2 Seeing _____ from God's point of view:

"... what are the riches of the glory of his inheritance in the saints ..."

3 Seeing our daily _____ from God's point of view:

"... and what is the exceeding greatness of his power towards us who believe."

The ministry of enlightenment is helping someone else in that crucial process.

ABC Theory of Emotion

Enlightenment involves changed thinking. The result for ourselves, or for those we come alongside, is that we see life, its problems and challenges in a different way.

A simple formula for understanding how our thoughts affect and influence the rest of our personality – particularly the feelings – is known as the ABC Theory of Emotion.

A = Activating Event

This represents any problem situation, happening or circumstance that is of a sufficient degree as to be threatening to a person's well-being.

B = Belief System

This is how we perceive or evaluate the way in which the problem event will have its impact upon us. The understanding we have about the event.

C = Consequent Emotion

This is the feeling or emotional distress that a person experiences because of what has been happening to them.

Remember:

> it is not **A** that controls **C**;
> it is **B** that controls **C**.

Circumstances do not make you feel the way you do. What causes your feelings (your reaction) is what you tell yourself about those events. Applying this understanding to our lives helps transform them.

Our emotions are the direct result of what we tell ourselves and our feelings follow. The real problem is not the circumstances so much as what produces these feelings – i.e. our belief system. It is how we react, not the circumstances, that produce the emotion. It is what we tell ourselves about the circumstances that produce how we feel.

Common Activating Events

One of the problems of being human is that we are all exposed to situations and events that can threaten our well-being at any moment.

Some examples of these are:

Marital difficulties
Redundancy
A broken friendship
A financial reverse
Criticism
Plans falling through
Serious sickness
Depressed environment

Our Belief System

It is not so much what happens to us but how we perceive it that brings about deep emotional distress. What we believe about an event, and how we perceive its impact upon us personally, contributes greatly to the degrees of emotional impact we will feel.

Our thoughts, or what we say to ourselves about an event, take two forms:

Rational and Irrational

Underlying almost all emotional upheaval there are three forms of irrational thinking:

1 _____

2 _____

3 _____

These thought disorders can split us apart emotionally. That's why the Bible is so emphatic that the truth sets us free. When we replace our awfulising, our demand-ingness, our self-devaluation with the truth, then there is no emotional disturbance. There may be some hurt, some fear, but there is no incapacitation for we have moved from the irrational to the rational.

The Consequent Emotions

There are many emotions that flow through the human heart, but experience and study show that the three dominant problem emotions are:

1 _____ and _____
Underneath these emotions is the thought disorder of
AWFULISING – "It would be awful if I failed".
E.g. The 12 spies – Numbers 13.

2 _____ and _____
Underneath these emotions is the thought disorder of
DEMANDINGNESS – "I should not be treated like this".
E.g. Moses – Numbers 20:10.

3 _____ and _____
Underneath these emotions is the thought disorder of
SELF-DEVALUATION – "I am a total failure".
E.g. Jeremiah – Lamentations 3:1–20.

IN SUMMARY

Caring Through Enlightenment

1   Knowing what is going on in our thinking is central to our understanding of ourselves.

2   The Bible everywhere emphasises the importance of the mind.

3   One of Satan's greatest strategies is to bring about spiritual disruption by infiltrating our minds.

4   Understanding the ABC Theory of Emotion helps us see that it is our thoughts that trigger our feelings:

A = Activating Event

B = Belief System

C = Consequent Emotion

CARE GROUP DISCUSSION

In your small groups review the video using the following questions and comments to stimulate your discussion. They are only guidelines to help you think through what you have viewed.

Remember! The goal here is to review the video material together.

1 **What are some of the things that go through your mind in church?**

2 **Talk through the Biblical aspects of the mind covered in the video.**

3 **Discuss the concept of self-talk.**

4 **Think through together the stages of foolish thinking.**

5 **Review the three elements of enlightenment.**

6 **How do you feel about the ABC Theory of Emotion? – think it through together.**

7 **Discuss any other items in the video presentation that you have thoughts on.**

Don't worry if you have not covered all the questions.

Caring

Triggering A Change

Week 5 – Personal Study

The Mind and Biblical Perspective

 Cross reference: video notes pages 168–169

Reading: Ephesians 4:17–32

"So I tell you this, and insist on it in the Lord, that you must no longer live as the Gentiles do, in the futility of their thinking." Ephesians 4:17

We are exploring the subject of Christian caring and the last video brought us to the third element of caring through enlightenment – bringing a changed perspective. We will now explore this further, recognising that it must be preceded by support through encouragement and hope and a sense of purpose through exhortation.

God has created us with the ability to think, the power to receive and process information. The information we process and how we process it has a deep effect and impact on our lives. In more recent years psychology has discovered the power and importance of the mind and acknowledges that life is not simply cause and effect but that the mind has a powerful influence.

"A man's life is what his thoughts make it." – Marcus Aurelius

"Change your thoughts and you change your world." – Norman Vincent Peale

"What I am to be I am now becoming." – President Roosevelt

"A man is not what he thinks he is, but what he thinks, HE is." – Anon

However, long before modern views the Bible highlighted the significance of the mind. There is no better book that speaks to the subject. Can you think of some of the things that the Bible says about the mind?

1 _____ Matthew 15:19

2 _____ Romans 8:7

3 _____ Romans 1:28

4 _____ Titus 1:15

5 _____ Ephesians 4:17

6 _____ Colossians 2:18

7 _____ 2 Corinthians 11:3

8 _____ James 1:8

9 _____ Isaiah 55:8–9

10 _____ Romans 12:2

11 _____ Isaiah 26:3

12 _____ Philippians 2:3

Write a summary sentence or two on the Biblical perspective of the mind:

_____

_____

_____

_____

_____

The New King James version of Proverbs 23:7 puts it like this:

"For as he thinks in his heart, so is he."

There can be no doubt that God views the mind as an important part of human functioning. Satan also recognises this fact and as with Eve seeks to level his seductive attacks in capturing and influencing our thoughts.

SPIRIT

SATAN'S ATTACK

MIND

EMOTIONS

WILL

– What we _____ about

– Affects the way we _____ and

– Influences the _____ we make.

Look up Genesis 3 verses 1–13.

1 What was the first thing the serpent did? (verse 1)

_____

_____

2 What was the second thing the serpent did? (verses 4–5)

_____

_____

3 What did he promise to expand? (verse 4)

_____

_____

4 What was the appeal of the fruit as presented by Satan? (verse 6)

_____

_____

In a sentence sum up Satan's attack on the first human pair.

_____

_____

_____

Look at Romans 1:21–25

How does Paul describe them?

They became _____

Their foolish hearts were _____

They exchanged the _____ for a _____

Can you think of a lie that Satan has presented to you in order to replace the truth of God's Word.

_____

_____

Satan knows that if he can capture our minds, he can capture our wills and affect our choices and decisions.

How did Jesus describe Satan? John 8:44

_____

_____

_____

What did Jesus declare? John 8:31–32

_____

_____

_____

Because we are tempted every day of our lives our thought processes become contaminated. Foolish thinking becomes a pattern from early childhood. When we are born of the Spirit of God our minds are then exposed to the power of God's Word to change and cleanse.

How did Paul express his concern for the Corinthians? 2 Corinthians 11:3

_____

_____

_____

Your mind is like a field for cultivating. Whatever you sow you will reap. "You" are quite neutral. If you sow seeds of hatred, you will reap hate. If you sow the Word of God you will reap a Godly life that radiates Christ. 1 Corinthians 3:9 states that we are God's husbandry. The Amplified New Testament translates it as "God's cultivated field."

We sow seeds in that field and each one brings forth after its own kind. Today you are a result of the thinking you sowed and the things you meditated on yesterday, or last year.

Read:

Ephesians 5:26

(The Church) "... to make her holy, cleansing her by _____

_____
"

Secular psychologists focus on changing the mind, from negative to positive, it is called cognitive restructuring, but the Biblical perspective is quite different because it talks about cleansing and renewing. The Biblical word for renewing means restoring back to its original condition, a mind in tune and harmony with its Creator.

"You were taught, with regard to your former way of life, to put off your old self, which is being corrupted by its deceitful desires; to be

_____

and to put on _____

_____

_____"Ephesians 4:22–24

List several areas of thinking that have been cleansed and made new in your life:

e.g. I am now a worthwhile person in God's eyes _____

_____

_____

_____

_____

Are there areas of your thinking that you struggle with?

e.g. Occasional doubt _____

_____

_____

_____

_____

This is why the Scripture says: *"Finally, brothers, whatever is true, whatever is noble, whatever is right, whatever is pure, whatever is lovely, whatever is admirable – if anything is excellent or praiseworthy – think about such things."* Philippians 4:8

Prayer: **Father, thank You for this wonderful ability to think and feel and decide. I echo the words of the psalmist today, may the words of my mouth and the meditations of my heart and mind, be acceptable to You O Lord. Amen.**

Care Practical Application:

_____

_____

_____

_____

Listening to Yourself

 Cross reference: video notes pages 169–170

Reading: Isaiah 55:1–9

> *"As the heavens are higher than the earth, so are my ways higher than your ways and my thoughts than your thoughts."* Isaiah 55:9

There is one person that you must live with for life, that's you, and there is one person that you must talk to for the rest of your life – guess who! This process is described as our self-talk or inner monologue. Sometimes we don't like to admit that we hold inner conversations with ourselves, but it's true to say that the voice we hear all day long is our own. As we saw in our sessions on exhortation, it is important not only to encourage, but to build hope and direction around people in the light of truth and grace. However, having achieved that, we need to put them in touch with some of the wrong perspectives they are holding. This is the ministry of enlightenment. As people go through life they develop a basic set of beliefs or value systems and this forms the basis of their self-talk. Everything else in life is filtered through, or gauged by it. It becomes the basis for living. We all carry on these inner conversations that begin at childhood and though largely unnoticed, affect our feelings, our reactions and to a large extent our behaviour. We come to believe what we tell ourselves, whether it is actually true or not.

List some of the things that mould our belief and value systems:

e.g. Parents_____   e.g. Education_____   _____

_____   _____   _____

_____   _____   _____

List a few basic beliefs that have come from these influences:

e.g. To trust others is a risky business_____

_____

_____

Can you identify any behavioural patterns that have arisen from these beliefs?

e.g. I am always suspicious of the motives of others _____

_____

_____

Our early years, or formative years as they are often described, have played an important role in developing our thinking patterns. We began thinking the way we now think at some time, or another, and more often than not our thoughts and beliefs originate during childhood and teenage development.

The experiences we had and the impressions we learned, although sometimes long forgotten, can still be having an impact upon us through our self-talk.

List three positive experiences you remember:

1 _____

2 _____

3 _____

List three negative experiences you remember:

1 _____

2 _____

3 _____

What do you say to yourself about these things today?:

_____

_____

_____

Listen to some of your inner conversations, identify some of your self-talk statements and write them down:

e.g. I bet John is angling for my job, I had better keep an eye on him. _____

_____

_____

This is an important exercise to regularly develop as it helps us begin to become aware of and identify the statements we make. Unless our beliefs and values are consistent with and based on truth, they are in fact misbeliefs.

As we said in the video, research has shown that we talk to ourselves at a rate of 1,300 words per minute.

Think of the following words for one minute each and write down some of the images and associated words and experiences they bring to mind.

Money _____

_____

_____

Rejection _____

_____

_____

Sin _____

_____

_____

Fear _____

_____

_____

Happiness _____

_____

_____

This will begin to help you to see what it is that you often say to yourself about these things. Sometimes our thoughts seem to be automatic and pop into our consciousness from nowhere. What random thoughts often pop into your mind?

1 _____

2 _____

3 _____

4 _____

5 _____

What is the statement you find repeating to yourself most often?

_____

_____

_____

Through these exercises I hope that you are beginning to recognise and identify some of your self-talk. This is what good carers are able to do in the ministry of enlightenment – to listen behind the words to recognise the thought patterns or as we are describing it here, the self-talk.

Optional Exercise

Look through the list of self-talk statements and tick those you recognise as ones you repeat to yourself.

Common Self-Talk Statements:

❏ 1   I should help everyone who needs it

❏ 2   I am inferior

❏ 3   God doesn't love me

❏ 4   I am too bad to be loved

❏ 5   It is terrible when things go wrong

❏ 6   Self-discipline is hard to achieve

❏ 7   Strong people don't ask for help

❏ 8   Anxiety is dangerous

❏ 9   My childhood will always affect me

❏ 10   I need to be sure in order to decide issues

❏ 11   I must look after number one

❏ 12   There is a perfect solution

❏ 13   Making a mistake is terrible

❏ 14   It is better not to tell people my problems

❏ 15   People will let me down

❏ 16   Knowing "why" is essential to my peace of mind

❏ 17   I should never upset anyone

❏ 18   If I am criticised I must be a bad person

❏ 19   Other people are a threat to me

❏ 20   I deserve to be punished for my mistakes

❏ 21   I am wrong if a person is hurt by my words and actions

❏ 22   I will get nothing out of giving pleasure to others

❏ 23   Crying out loud is a sign of weakness and immaturity

❏ 24   If people cared for me they would know what I want

❏ 25   Emotions will only interfere with my ability to succeed

❏ 26   People are not to be trusted

❏ 27   There are ways in which I am defective as a person

❏ 28   It is better to keep my thoughts to myself

❏ 29   People should trust me

❏ 30   People must love me if I am to feel good

❏ 31   People should be condemned when they do wrong

❏ 32   I must do everything "perfectly" or I will not feel good

❏ 33   People ought to follow the advice I give

❏ 34   Possible is the same as probable

❏ 35   I ought to do better … I ought to do better

❏ 36   I can't change what I think

❏ 37   Christians must never get upset

❏ 38   I must never show weakness

❏ 39   What's the use? Giving up is the best policy

❏ 40   I must never tell people how I feel – they might dislike me

❏ 41   The more I please people, the more they will like me

❏ 42   It is terrible if people don't like me

❏ 43   I am unattractive

❏ 44   I have no talents

❏ 45   I will never be any good

❏ 46   I must get what I want in order to be happy

❏ 47   I can't stand it if people don't like me

❏ 48   I am stupid

❏ 49   I can't do anything right

❏ 50   There I go again

Today's assignment is designed to develop your awareness of the power and influence of your thought processes. Between now and your next assignment develop your ability to tune in and listen to yourself.

As you develop this skill in relation to yourself you will find that as you come alongside others to care for them you will begin to tune in to their self-talk and help them to recognise it at the appropriate time.

Prayer: **Father, help me to be more aware of the power and influence of my own thoughts. Where there are negative ones give me grace to recognise them in the light of Your truth, which alone can set me free to think as You would have me think. Amen.**

Care Practical Application:

_____

_____

_____

Foolish Thinking

 Cross reference: video notes pages 170–171

Reading: 1 Corinthians 13

> *"When I was a child, I talked like a child, I thought like a child, I reasoned like a child. When I became a man, I put childish ways behind me."* 1 Corinthians 13:11

As we saw in Day 2, our thinking patterns develop early in childhood. Paul in our passage today, says, that when he was a child, he thought like a child. We know that a child thinks primarily about one thing – itself. It is very self-centred. Wash me, feed me, carry me, change me, clothe me, ... me, ... me, ... me. The legacy of the Fall is that sin has made us self-centred and self-focused, so that as our thinking patterns develop from early childhood, they become very self-centred. As we get older, they move from being just self-centred into being self-sufficient. This pushes out of our lives any need of God as we think that we can manage life quite nicely by ourselves. When we refuse to allow God to be the centre of our lives, the Bible describes us as a fool.

> *"The fool says in his heart there is no God."* Psalm 14:1

Read:

Luke 12:16–21

What word occurs six times in this passage? _____

What word occurs five times in this passage?_____

Why did God describe him as a fool? _____

_____

Within the human heart there is a stubborn commitment to independence, to the belief that I can handle life best on my own. Part of the process of enlightenment is helping people to recognise and identify their foolish thinking, how it has developed and how they continue to hold on to it, to try and hold their lives together. Unless something dramatic happens to us to bring about changes in our attitudes we soon become "professional" foolish thinkers. On the video presentation we highlighted the eight stages of Foolishness.

List a characteristic you may have observed of these stages of foolishness.

Year

0–1   Naive Foolishness   e.g. I am the centre of the universe   _____

2–6   Learned Foolishness   e.g. If I howl long enough, I will get my own way _____

7–12   Practised Foolishness   _____

13–18 Disappointed Foolishness   _____

19–30 Rearranged Foolishness   _____

31–65 Stable Foolishness   _____

66 +   Bankrupt Foolishness   _____

        Eternal Foolishness   _____

"Do not deceive yourselves. If any one of you thinks he is wise by the standards of this age, he should become a 'fool' so that he may become wise. For the wisdom of this world is foolishness in God's sight. As it is written: 'He catches the wise in their craftiness.'" 1 Corinthians 3:18–19

The error people make in life is thinking that the solution to our personal problems depends on changing and improving our circumstances, or by changing the way we feel about things:

e.g. I'd feel happy if ...

     – my husband treated me better
     – I had more friends
     – I was more successful at my job
     – I wasn't single
     – my parents hadn't rejected me
     – the people at church treated me better
     – I had more money and a better home.

e.g. My life would be complete if ...

- I didn't feel so depressed
- I felt warmer towards my wife
- my craving for food was not so overwhelming
- I didn't feel so rejected
- I could just stop being so anxious or worried
- I felt better about myself
- my fear of failure was taken away.

As you consider these statements do you consider them to be legitimate desires – give reasons for your answers:

_____

_____

_____

As you consider these statements again, what do you think is the foolish thinking underlying them:

_____

_____

_____

Can you see a link between answers to these two questions:

_____

_____

_____

As you think about your own life, what have been some areas of foolish thinking?

1 _____

2 _____

3 _____

What is the opposite of foolishness?_____

Write out a definition of …

Foolishness

_____

_____

_____

Wisdom

_____

_____

_____

In relation to the stages of life listed below, can you think of a Biblical word of wisdom you might be able to apply?

Naive Foolishness e.g. A child should not be left to his own foolishness (Prov 29:15)

_____

Learned Foolishness e.g. A child needs a clear framework of reference (Prov 22:6)

_____

Practised Foolishness_____

_____

Disappointed Foolishness _____

_____

Re-arranged Foolishness_____

_____

Stable Foolishness_____

_____

Bankrupt Foolishness _____

_____

Eternal Foolishness _____

_____

"For this reason, since the day we heard about you, we have not stopped praying for you and asking God to fill you with the knowledge of his will through all spiritual wisdom and understanding." Colossians 1:9

"My purpose is that they may be encouraged in heart and united in love, so that they may have the full riches of complete understanding, in order that they may know the mystery of God, namely, Christ, in whom are hidden all the treasures of wisdom and knowledge." Colossians 2:2–3

Prayer: **At best Lord my human wisdom is folly in Your sight. Take my foolish thoughts, Lord, and through the power of Your Word and the revelation of Your Holy Spirit, impart to me Your divine wisdom. Amen.**

Care Practical Application:

_____

_____

_____

Enlightenment

 Cross reference: video notes pages 171–172

 Reading: Ephesians 1:15–20

> *"I pray also that the eyes of your heart may be enlightened in order that you may know the hope to which he has called you, the riches of his glorious inheritance in the saints ..."* Ephesians 1:18

We have said that enlightenment is changing the foolish independent thinking that causes us to try and handle life on our own.

Write out the video definition:

The ministry of enlightenment is _____

_____

Although the word enlighten or enlightenment is found only a few times in Scripture, it is clear that changed thinking is a key concept in the Word of God. Three elements were highlighted in the video presentation to focus on when we are caring for people going through difficult times.

1   Helping Them See the Future from God's Point of View

Some important principles to follow

    1   Explore how they view the future
    2   Understand their concern for the future
    3   Establish what in the future holds fear for them
    4   Don't minimise their concern for the future
    5   Don't offer false hope
    6   Don't promise changes that may not materialise

How might people's expectation of the future have been influenced?

e.g. need to be successful _____   _____

_____   _____   _____

How might people's disillusionment of the future be based in the past?

e.g. past disappointment _____ _____

_____ _____ _____

What might be some of the statements that people are making to themselves about the future?

1 _____

2 _____

3 _____

What are some key elements about the future from God's perspective?

1 _____

2 _____

3 _____

"'For I know the plans I have for you,' declares the Lord, 'plans to prosper you and not to harm you, plans to give you hope and a future.'" Jeremiah 29:11

2 Seeing Ourselves from God's Point of View

Some important principles to follow

1 Explore how self-image has been developed
2 Explore why they are unhappy with themselves
3 Understand their feelings of worthlessness
4 Don't minimise the strength of their feelings
5 Don't underestimate the strength of other people's influence
6 Don't patronise them

How might a person's view of themselves have been influenced?

e.g. physical deficiency _____ _____ _____

_____ _____ _____

What might be the preoccupation of someone with low self-esteem?

e.g. people pleasing _____ _____ _____

_____ _____ _____

What might be some of the statements that people with low self-esteem may be saying to themselves?

1 _____

_____

2 _____

_____

3 _____

_____

What are some key elements about self acceptance from a Biblical perspective?

1 _____

2 _____

3 _____

"For you created my inmost being; you knit me together in my mother's womb. I praise you because I am fearfully and wonderfully made; your works are wonderful, I know that full well. My frame was not hidden from you when I was made in the secret place. When I was woven together in the depths of the earth, your eyes saw my unformed body. All the days ordained for me were written in your book before one of them came to be." Psalm 139:13–16

3 Helping to See our Daily Resources from God's Point of View

Some important principles to follow

1. Explore why their resources are deficient.
2. Understand their feelings of personal bankruptcy.
3. Establish exactly what resources they do have.
4. Don't try and convince them they have what they haven't.
5. Don't encourage them beyond the realistic possibilities.
6. Don't underestimate their sense of desperation.

What are some of the resources that people come to depend on?

e.g. People _____   _____   _____

_____   _____   _____

What are some of the resources that God has provided?

e.g. Grace _____   _____   _____

_____   _____   _____

What statements might people be saying to themselves about their lack of resources?

1 _____

2 _____

3 _____

Can you think of some Biblical examples of God replenishing expended resources for people?

Person	Instance
e.g. Elijah	When God sent the angel
_____	_____

"And my God will meet all your needs according to his glorious riches in Christ Jesus."
Philippians 4:19

Prayer: Lord, I acknowledge that only Your Word can bring insight, revelation and enlightenment to those who struggle to cope with life. May I be the ray of light that You can use to drive away their darkness. Amen.

Care Practical Application:

_____

_____

_____

Learning the ABC

 Cross reference: video notes pages 172–174

 Reading: Numbers 13:26–14:9

> *"We saw the Nephilim there (the descendants of Anak come from the Nephilim). We seemed like grasshoppers in our own eyes, and we looked the same to them."*
> Numbers 13:33

We have been seeing the significant influence of the mind upon life attitudes and the behaviour patterns of people's lives. Enlightenment is helping people to begin to see that for themselves, to understand something of the thinking pattern that they may be unaware of, that is underlying the difficulties they are struggling with. Everyone understands their basic ABC, and helping them to see the pattern of their life circumstances is also as easy as ABC, everyone can understand it. Your goal as a carer, after encouraging (support) and exhorting (hope in the context of grace and truth) is to enlighten (bring a Biblical perspective) and the ABC theory of emotion is a helpful way to enable someone to grasp what the process entails.

A = _____

B = _____

C = _____

From the video presentation write out in a sentence what the ABC theory of emotion is:

_____

_____

_____

It is not so much what happens to us, although we often feel the immediate impact of that but how we evaluate it in our mind, that's important. It is often not the event in itself, but how we interpret that event as it relates to us.

Exercise:

A Someone criticises you

B _____ – what might you be saying to yourself?

C You feel bad

A Someone criticises you

B _____ – what might you be saying to yourself?

C You feel good

Most of us "set ourselves up" because of the things that we tell ourselves and as we have seen, for many of us, those thinking patterns become a way of life. We are seeing that emotions do not function in a vacuum but are triggered as a result of the life events that impact our thought processes.

A Activating Events

Some life events can be avoided and others changed. If that is the case, then we have a possibility and a responsibility to do something about it. However, as we saw in the video, there are often circumstances in our lives over which we have no control.

What are some difficult life circumstances that people you know are currently struggling with?

Circumstance	Person
1 _____	_____
2 _____	_____
3 _____	_____

Take a moment to pray for them.

What is a particular life circumstance that you have struggled with?

_____

The ABC theory of emotion says it's not only what happens to us in life that affects us, but what we tell ourselves, that determines our responses.

B Belief System

Our perception of the consequences of a life event are triggered almost instantaneously, based on the existing thought patterns. As we have seen, God has designed us in such a way that what we think about affects the way we feel, which determines our responses and actions. We suggested in the video presentation that these automatic thought responses take one or two forms.

Rational – Thoughts based on Truth and Reality.
The truth may be painful but in the context of grace and God's perspective can never destroy us.

Irrational – Thoughts based on untruth and unreality.
Misbelief and lies will always cripple and be debilitating and will always end up destroying those things we hold dear.

Most of us when responding to a life event, because of past life experience, more often than not do so with irrational and therefore faulty thinking. The ministry of enlightenment is exposing that irrational thinking in the light of Biblical truth.

Three major forms of irrational thought

1 *Awfulising* – This is when we magnify an event beyond its proper proportions and exaggerate it in our thinking so that it becomes overwhelming and totally intimidating.

Write out an awfulising statement using as many descriptive words as you can.

_____

_____

2 *Demandingness* – This is when we want things to go the way we think they must or should, and when they don't, we can't handle it and demand that they change.

Write out a statement of demandingness.

_____

_____

3 *Self-Devaluation* – This is when we denigrate or belittle ourselves to the point of self ridicule and humiliation. We become full of self-pity and come to the conclusion, I am just not a worthwhile person.

Write out a statement of self-devaluation.

_____

_____

Look at the passage you read today. Write out the irrational statements of the Children of Israel.

1 Awfulising (Numbers 14:3)

_____

_____

2 Demanding (Numbers 14:4)

_____

_____

3 Self-Devaluation (Numbers 13:33)

_____

_____

Write out the rational response from Joshua and Caleb (Numbers 14:7–9)

_____

_____

_____

C   **Consequent Emotion**

The dominant emotions that we have looked at previously, we can now see are linked to our irrational thoughts.

Fear and Anxiety – Awfulising

You are asked to make a public speech, you are terrified at the prospect and your thoughts are:

1   I might make a mess of it, that would be catastrophic.

Fear of _____

2   People might not accept what I say, that would be unbearable.

Fear of _____

3   I might make myself look foolish, that would be terrible.

Fear of _____

4   I might not perform well, that would be devastating.

Fear of _____

What statements of truth might you counteract these irrational thoughts with?

_____

_____

Anger and Resentment – Demandingness

Plans have been discussed and decisions taken without your involvement, you feel greatly upset and your thoughts are:

1   My view should have been considered, I demand that they reconsider their decision.

   Feelings of _____

2   They ought to have consulted me first, I demand they listen to my views on this.

   Feelings of _____

3   I had a right to know about this, I demand a full and complete explanation.

   Feelings of _____

4   I should not be treated in this way, I demand an immediate apology.

   Feelings of _____

Write out a statement of truth that you might counteract these thoughts with.

_____

_____

Guilt and Shame – Self-devaluation

You had a besetting sin and were deeply challenged about it. You dealt with it at the Cross some time ago, but you were recently tempted again and gave in to the temptation. Your thoughts are:

1   I am a terrible person, if people knew what I was really like they would not readily accept and love me.

   Feelings of _____

2 I am a total failure, I really always have been and guess I always will be, however hard I try.

   Feelings of _____

3 I am utterly hopeless and worthless, if I was a better person, I'd be a victorious Christian.

   Feelings of _____

4 No matter how much effort I make, it's obvious that I'm not good enough, there is no hope in going on in my Christian life.

   Feelings of _____

Write out a statement of truth that you might counteract these thoughts with.

_____

_____

The ABC then is more than a theory, it is a working principle. The ministry of enlightenment is helping people to see how God created us and how Satan has produced negative thinking by building irrational thought processes that divert our attention away from the truth and perspective of God's Word.

Prayer: **I can see how easily life's circumstances can overwhelm people and deeply affect them emotionally. Father, only Your Word can bring stability and perspective. Make me an able minister of Your truth I pray. Amen.**

Care Practical Application:

_____

_____

_____

Care Group Review

Spend 50–60 minutes interacting together on the responses you have written down in your own personal study.

Spend about 10–12 minutes for each day with each member of the group having an opportunity to reflect and discuss their responses.

Notes on the Discussion

Day 1

_____

_____

_____

Day 2

_____

_____

_____

Day 3

_____

_____

_____

Day 4

_____

_____

_____

Day 5

_____

_____

_____

Share how you are getting on with your Care Practical Application

Conclusions for the week:

_____

_____

_____

_____

_____

_____

Programme 6

Caring

A Whole New Perspective

Gaining the Right Perspective

D = Dispute Wrong Thoughts

We have seen how problem-causing beliefs affect our lives. If we are to live effectively, we must learn how to combat these beliefs. You cannot change your thinking until you've disputed the wrong thoughts.

In 2 Corinthians 10:4–5 (NKJ), we are shown that a fierce battle can take place in the mind. But we are promised God's help in this fight against problem-causing thoughts.

"For the weapons of our warfare are not carnal but mighty in God for pulling down strongholds, casting down arguments and every high thing that exalts itself against the knowledge of God, bringing every thought into captivity to the obedience of Christ."

The following steps have been found to be helpful in bringing irrational and unhelpful thoughts into captivity:

1   Identify them

2   Write them down

3   Vigorously challenge them

E = Exchange Wrong Beliefs for Right Beliefs

Effective Christian living depends to a great extent on how expert we are at putting God's thoughts in the place of our thoughts.

Principles to follow when exchanging right beliefs for wrong beliefs are as follows:

1   Counter with statement of _____

2   Reinforce with _____

3 _____ **it down**

4 _____ **scripture**

Tips for memorising Scripture:

a   Read it slowly and repeatedly
b   Write it out several times
c   Underline the key words
d   Say it out loud

5   Meditate on it frequently

IN SUMMARY

The ABC Theory of Emotion

A = Activating Event

B = Belief System

C = Consequent Emotion

D = Dispute

E = Exchange

PROBLEM RESOLVING CHART

EXAMPLE

A = The Event

The activating event that gave rise to my problem was

Wounding criticism as a result of failure to complete a task

B = The Belief

The things I have been saying to myself could be

I should not be treated in this way

People think badly of me

C = The Consequent Emotion

The feelings I experienced in the presence of the events were

Anger and resentment

Guilt and shame

The intensity on a scale of 1 to 10 was

1   2   3   4   5   6   7   8   (9)   10   (circle appropriate figure)

D = The Dispute

The thought I am to dispute is

I deserve to be treated better

I'm a hopeless failure

E = The Exchange

The new thought I am to hold in my mind and reinforce with God's Word is:
Thought:

God loves me and forgives me.

I am worthwhile in the sight of God

Scripture:

Colossians 2:13–14

Ephesians 2:8–10

PROBLEM RESOLVING CHART

A = The Event

The activating event that gave rise to my problem was

_____

_____

B = The Belief

The things I have been saying to myself could be

_____

_____

C = The Consequent Emotion

The feelings I experienced in the presence of the events were

_____

_____

The intensity on a scale of 1 to 10 was

1   2   3   4   5   6   7   8   9   10   (circle appropriate figure)

D = The Dispute

The thought I am to dispute is

_____

_____

E = The Exchange

The new thought I am to hold in my mind and reinforce with God's Word is:

Thought: _____

Scripture: _____

Renewing the Mind

The key to having Christ's mind in our mind is simple, but requires much dedication and commitment. Memorisation and meditation are two crucial words in building up our minds.

Allowing God's Word to infiltrate the mind results in the following:

1 _____ **our minds**

The reconstruction of our minds comes from memorising and meditating on the Word of God regularly. The long-standing thought patterns and structures are changed by the Word of God. Nothing is more influential to the personality than to think God's thoughts after Him.

2 _____ **our emotions**

The Word of God, when it impacts the mind, acts upon the emotions in a powerful way. It not only assures positive emotions, but enables us to enjoy the full expression of our emotions. The more we accept God's Word into our minds, the more our emotions will become obedient to the Word of God.

3 _____ **the will**

The will is also greatly influenced by what we think and what we believe. When our thinking is in line with truth, then the will functions in the way it was designed. It's easier to choose God's way when you're thinking His thoughts.

> *"... I think of you through the watches of the night. Because you are my help ..."*
> Psalm 63:6,7

IN SUMMARY

A New Perspective

1   Learn to identify wrong thoughts

2   Write them down and dispute them

3   Exchange them for the truth that is found in Scripture

4   Memorise and meditate on God's Word, especially before
    you go to sleep

What is the Impact on the Church?

The whole point of taking the Scriptures into our minds is so that we can begin to think with the mind of Christ.

Imagine what it would be like in a church full of people whose minds were enlightened in this way and who were able to maintain that way of thinking through continually meditating on the Scriptures. There would be:

1   **A deeper spiritual bond**

2   **Stronger spiritual assurance**

3   **Clearer corporate guidance**

4   **Better physical health**

5   **Greater faith and confidence**

It is not God's responsibility to change the tapes you are playing to yourself, but yours. He has given you His Word to read, to meditate upon, and to take on board. That's the clear path to spiritual growth and to enlightenment – the reconstruction of the mind.

Remember: the more you practise these principles in your own life, the more you will be able to help others too.

CARE GROUP DISCUSSION

In your small groups review the video using the following questions and comments to stimulate your discussion. They are only guidelines to help you think through what you have viewed.

1 **Discuss the concept of disputing wrong thoughts.**

2 **What did you feel about the process of "exchanging"?**

3 **Any comments on the A B C D E approach?**

4 **What did you struggle with most on this exercise?**

5 **Talk through the concept of the mind of Christ.**

6 **Review the elements involved in renewing the mind.**

Don't worry if you have not covered all the questions.

Programme 6

Caring

A Whole New Perspective

Week 6 – Personal Study

Taking Thoughts Captive

📺 **Cross reference: video notes pages 211–212**

📖 **Reading: 2 Corinthians 10:1–6**

> *"The weapons we fight with are not the weapons of the world. On the contrary, they have divine power to demolish strongholds. We demolish arguments and every pretension that sets itself up against the knowledge of God, and we take captive every thought to make it obedient to Christ."* 2 Corinthians 10:4–5

We have seen how problem-causing thought patterns play a major role in our lives. If we are to help people effectively and care for them by bringing a new perspective, we need to help them to combat their irrational beliefs.

Disputing Wrong Thoughts

Paul mentions three different areas in 2 Corinthians 10:3–5 that we are able to demolish. Write them down:

1 v4 _____ – castle, fortress, tower

2 v5 _____ – imagination

3 v5 _____ – fake, forgery not genuine article

and one area to take captive

4 v5 _____ – self-talk

Write out a definition of "demolish".

_____

_____

_____

Example

		Exercise One	Exercise Two
1 THOUGHT (Negative self-talk.)	I am of no value	"Acceptance is the most important thing in my life"	"Everything I do must be perfect"
2 PRETENSION (Accepting it as if it were the truth.)	Therefore I am inferior to others.		
3 ARGUMENT (Life experience reinforces it.)	Because others are always better than me.		
4 STRONGHOLD (A strong belief that governs life.)	Developing into a debilitating inferiority complex.		

What does Paul say the pretension does?

_____

What does it mean to take a thought captive?

_____

_____

_____

Exercise:

The children are now off hand and Mary decides to re-enter the job market. She has no formal qualifications and feels she was only pretty average at school which was some years ago now. Although she has tried to maintain her figure in recent years, she has battled with a weight problem. She is finding it difficult to sum up courage to put in a job application for additional help at the local primary school. As she talks to you she seems full of anxiety and says, "I'll probably be turned down even if I do apply. They are not looking for any qualifications, she says, but I expect that they are looking for some young slender thing with a lot of energy. What with bringing up the children my figure and energy levels are not what they used to be and I know that I'm terribly overweight. I never was very bright at school anyway."

Explore the following steps in order to establish a plan for helping Mary to take her irrational thoughts captive to Christ.

1 Identify them

   ◆ **Explore their origins**
   ◆ **What kind of situations do they relate to now?**
   ◆ **What is their emotional impact now?**
   ◆ **Categorize them**   **– awfulising**

                                    – demanding

                                    – self-devaluating

HYPOTHESISE

What irrational thoughts do you think might be going on in Mary's mind?

_____

_____

_____

What might be their origin?

_____

_____

_____

What is the emotional impact now?

_____

_____

_____

How would you categorise the thoughts?

_____

_____

_____

In a couple of sentences identify back to Mary what you consider her irrational thoughts might be:

_____

_____

_____

2 Write them down

Getting someone to write their irrational thoughts down helps them to crystallize these thoughts as they see them expressed in their own handwriting.

   ◆ **get them to admit the irrational thought**

   ◆ **get them to write it down themselves**

   ◆ **get them to write down its emotional consequences**

   ◆ **get them to identify the category**

What would you be looking for Mary to write down in a sentence?

_____

_____

_____

3 Vigorously challenge them

When something or someone is taken captive, it usually takes vigorous effort. Often it has to be forceful because there is a struggle. Remember these irrational thoughts have:

    1 Pretended to be the truth
    2 Have exalted themselves in place of the truth
    3 Have set themselves against the knowledge of the truth

Having identified them and written them down, they must now be exposed for what they are, nothing but lies.

◆ **Get a clear acknowledgement that it is recognised as being a lie.**

◆ **Having captured it, take control of it.**

◆ **Bring it in prayer to the Cross – the place of death.**

◆ **Confess the sin of choosing to believe a lie.**

◆ **Submit it to the Lordship of Christ.**

Can you think of some of the weapons at our disposal for tearing down strongholds, arguments, pretensions and irrational thoughts:

_____   _____   _____

_____   _____   _____

What might you say to Mary as you help her to take captive her irrational thoughts:

_____

_____

_____

As you have been working through these exercises have you become aware of irrational thoughts that you need to take captive? Write them down:

_____

_____

_____

Follow the steps you would have done with Mary.

Prayer: Father, I am grateful for the awesome power of Your Word, with its ability to expose my faulty and irrational thinking in the light of Your eternal truth. Amen.

Care Practical Application:

_____

_____

_____

Replacing Irrational Thoughts

📺 **Cross reference: video notes pages 211–212**

📖 **Reading: Psalm 119:97–105**

> *"I gain understanding from your precepts; therefore I hate every wrong path. Your word is a lamp to my feet and a light for my path."* Psalm 119:104–105

Once you know something is a lie, because it has been exposed as a lie and you have accepted it as such, it is then hard to convince yourself that it is actually the truth. D L Moody said, if a stick is crooked, put a straight one alongside it and it is plain for all to see. To expose the lie put the truth alongside it and then embrace it.

> *"Finally, brothers, whatever is true, whatever is noble, whatever is right, whatever is pure, whatever is lovely, whatever is admirable – if anything is excellent or praise-worthy – think about such things."* Philippians 4:8

Write out your own definition of an irrational thought:

_____

_____

_____

Our effectiveness in the Christian life depends to a great extent on how good we become at recognising irrational thoughts, and our ability to replace them with God's thoughts.

There are three key steps in mastering this process, and the more you practise them the more you will be able to help others discover a new perspective through your caring relationship:

1   Recognise irrational thought patterns
2   Construct a statement that is in harmony with the truth
3   Reinforce it with a verse or passage from Scripture

Example:

WRONG BELIEF	RIGHT BELIEF	SCRIPTURE
I am so hopeless, even when I do my best I never seem to get it right. I guess I'll always just be a stupid person.	With Jesus there is always hope. I know it pleases Him when I do my best. Others may think of me as being stupid, but He sees me as His special child.	He chose the lowly things of this world and the despised things – and the things that are not – to nullify the things that are, so that no-one may boast before him. 1 Corinthians 1:28–29

Work through the following exercise, changing the wrong belief by constructing a right belief and then working out a Scripture that confirms it.

WRONG BELIEF	RIGHT BELIEF	SCRIPTURE
I am so lonely and no-one really cares about me		
I am unattractive and people don't like me, I'm just an uninteresting person		
Other people should listen to me, they ignore my ideas and suggestions.		

WRONG BELIEF	RIGHT BELIEF	SCRIPTURE
If only my wife would change, I would find her easier to love.		
I know it's wrong, but it's the only bit of pleasure I get out of life these days.		
I just can't stand to be criticised, it devastates me and then I find myself justifying myself.		

Optional Exercise

WRONG BELIEF	RIGHT BELIEF	SCRIPTURE
I thought when he married me, he would treat me with love, tenderness and consideration. I think he owes it to me to behave better.		
My work is so important to me, I love it, it gives me such a buzz and I really enjoy the fruit of my labour.		

WRONG BELIEF	RIGHT BELIEF	SCRIPTURE
I've given up on church, they're supposed to be caring and loving, and all they do is argue and talk behind each other's back.		
I can't seem to forgive myself, I know I should not have let this happen but it has, and it's ruined people's lives.		
I'm not sure that I can continue on now that he's gone, we had so many happy years together, I'm on my own now.		

As you work with this principle in your own life you will be able to help others find a new freedom as you encourage them to embrace the truth:

"Then you will know the truth, and the truth will set you free." John 8:32

Prayer: Thank You for the reality of Your Word, which declares "He who the Son sets free is free indeed." Amen.

Care Practical Application:

_____

_____

_____

Engrafting the Truth

📺 **Cross reference: video notes pages 213–215**

📖 **Reading: Psalm 119:33–56**

> *"I will speak of your statutes before kings and will not be put to shame, for I delight in your commands because I love them."* Psalm 119:46–47

We have seen then that effective caring for people, is first supporting them, coming alongside to understand and to encourage them. The danger with the ministry of enlightenment is that we jump straight in with the ABC theory, without taking time to first encourage and support. Following encouragement we need to move on to exhortation, exploring not just the immediate life circumstances but some of the feelings that are going on inside the person, that they are seeking to cope with. Undergirding them with a sense of hope and direction. Remember, you cannot effectively exhort an unencouraged person, people want to know how much you care, they do not care how much you know. Exhortation we have said is helping a person respond to life in accordance with God's will and Word bringing hope, direction and purpose. We do this by ministering grace in the context of truth. Can you remember the four important aspects of grace and truth that we exhort people towards?

1 _____

2 _____

3 _____

4 _____

Following encouragement and exhortation, we are then seeking to change a person's perspective through changing previous thinking patterns and replacing them with Biblical thinking patterns. We have given you a simple tool of A,B,C,D,E to help people with this process. Your understanding and mastery of this framework is important to an effective ministry of enlightenment. You have already had an opportunity to use the problem resolving chart but this is a training tool, not something you would actually use when caring for someone. The elements and process need to be committed to your memory, so that you can lead someone verbally through the process. We know that practice makes perfect and we want you to practise again today. Remember, it is a framework not a formula.

You have two charts today and this is what we want you to do:

1 Think of an activating event in your own life and work through the ABC process with the first chart (see page 233)

2 Ask someone else to help you by sharing an activating event and work with them through the ABC with the second chart (see page 234)

3 Ask someone else to help you by sharing an activating event and work through the ABC process with them, without the chart, but from memory.

Sum up in a few sentences how you got on, and how well you feel you have grasped the process and committed it to memory:

_____

_____

_____

_____

_____

Prayer: **Lord, help me not to see this process as some sort of slick technique to put people through. Help me to realise that it is an opportunity for Your Holy Spirit to apply Your life changing truth to those in need whom I am seeking to care for. Amen.**

Care Practical Application:

_____

_____

_____

PROBLEM RESOLVING CHART

A = The Event

The activating event that gave rise to my problem was

_____

_____

B = The Belief

The things I have been saying to myself could be

_____

_____

C = The Consequent Emotion

The feelings I experienced in the presence of the events were

_____

_____

The intensity on a scale of 1 to 10 was

1   2   3   4   5   6   7   8   9   10   (circle appropriate figure)

D = The Dispute

The thought I am to dispute is

_____

_____

E = The Exchange

The new thought I am to hold in my mind and reinforce with God's Word is:

Thought: _____

Scripture: _____

PROBLEM RESOLVING CHART

A = The Event

The activating event that gave rise to my problem was

_____

_____

B = The Belief

The things I have been saying to myself could be

_____

_____

C = The Consequent Emotion

The feelings I experienced in the presence of the events were

_____

_____

The intensity on a scale of 1 to 10 was

1   2   3   4   5   6   7   8   9   10   (circle appropriate figure)

D = The Dispute

The thought I am to dispute is

_____

_____

E = The Exchange

The new thought I am to hold in my mind and reinforce with God's Word is:

Thought: _____

Scripture: _____

Developing the Mind of Christ

 Cross reference: video notes page 216

 Reading: Joshua 1:1–8

> *"Do not let this Book of the Law depart from your mouth; meditate on it day and night, so that you may be careful to do everything written in it. Then you will be prosperous and successful." Joshua 1:8*

Having helped someone to challenge and change their thinking, we need finally to encourage them to continue to meditate and focus on God's Word, committing to memory the truths they discover within it, in order that their perspective on life will remain a spiritual one.

Biblical meditation is the process of holding a phrase or verse of Scripture in the mind, pondering on it, continually contemplating it, dwelling on it, viewing it from every angle of the imagination, until it begins to affect the deepest part of one's spiritual being.

Andrew Murray defines it as "holding the Word of God in the mind until it has affected every area of one's life and character".

Campbell McAlpine says, "Meditation is the devotional practice of pondering the words of a verse or verses of scripture, with a receptive heart, allowing the Holy Spirit to take the written word and applying it as the living word to the inner being".

Psalm 1:2 *"... on _____ he **meditates** day and night."*

The word used here is HAGAH which means to murmur (in pleasure), to ponder. Meditation is a pleasant "murmuring" of Scripture to oneself.

Psalm 119:99 *"... for I **meditate** on _____."*

The word used here is SICHAM which means to reflect with deep devotion; to contemplate. Meditation is that quiet contemplation of and reflection on Scripture.

Psalm 19:14 *"... _____ be pleasing in your sight, O Lord."*

The word used here is HIGGAYON which means a musical rotation, a murmuring sound. Meditation is a musical repetition of God's Word.

1 Timothy 4:15 *"***Meditate** *upon* _____.*"* (NKJ)

The word here is MELETAO which means to ponder carefully with the mind; to muse upon. Meditation is a careful and prayerful reviewing of Scripture.

Write down your own definition of Biblical meditation:

_____

_____

_____

Scripture suggests that there are four occasions when we have opportunity to meditate on the truths of God's Word. Read Deuteronomy 6:7; Psalm 63:5–6.

1 _____

   This means during times of rest and relaxation.

2 _____

   This means when you go from place to place and your mind is free.

3 _____

   This means as you lay down and prepare to go to sleep at night.

4 _____

   This means when you arise first thing before you get into the activities of the day.

Meditation on God's Word impacts three major areas of human functioning:

1 Reconstruction of Our Thought Life

God's thoughts are contained in His Word. As our minds absorb His Word, our own thought "patterning" from the world is challenged.

A RENEWED MIND – Romans 12:2

Be not _____	–	SUSCHĒMATIZŌ – to be patterned after
But be ye _____	–	METAMORPHOŌ – to change into another form
By the _____	–	ANAKAINOŌ – to make new again as original condition

Whatsoever things are:

_____   _____

_____   _____

_____   _____

think on these things (Philippians 4:8, AV)

The world gains its understanding about life from observation, learning and experience. However, much of the knowledge in today's world is based on humanistic assumptions and conclusions. A Christian who meditates on God's Word will experience an understanding of life, that will lift him above the negative thinking of the world.

2 Refocus the Emotions

Because what we think about affects the way we feel, as our thought structures change, our emotions begin to respond. The Bible is full of emotion. When the Holy Spirit inspired its writers, it was when they were expressing deep emotion, like Jeremiah, Job, Isaiah and many more. One of the widest spectrums of human emotion is found in the Book of Psalms. It is a wonderful book for meditation. Cast your eye over a selection of Psalms and write down the emotion expressed and its reference:

1 _____ Ref: _____

2 _____ Ref: _____

3 _____ Ref: _____

4 _____ Ref: _____

5 _____ Ref: _____

6 _____ Ref: _____

7 _____ Ref: _____

8 _____ Ref: _____

9 _____ Ref: _____

10_____ Ref: _____

3 Redirection of the Will

As the Word of God begins to flow into the personality the will becomes subject to the influences of God's Word. As truth becomes the influencing factor of our thinking, the principles of God's Word begin to determine the direction of our will. As His thoughts become our thoughts then His will becomes our desire. As the human will responds to the divine will, we are able to say with the Psalmist, *"I delight to do thy will, O my God"*.

Can you think of ten aspects of God's will that are revealed in His Word.

1 _____ Ref: _____

2 _____ Ref: _____

3 _____ Ref: _____

4 _____ Ref: _____

5 _____ Ref: _____

6 _____   Ref: _____

7 _____   Ref: _____

8 _____   Ref: _____

9 _____   Ref: _____

10 _____   Ref: _____

Prayer: Father I am conscious that my mind is so often influenced by the things around me. I thank You for Your Word that renews my mind and that through it I can receive the mind of Christ. Amen.

Care Practical Application:

_____

_____

_____

An Example of Caring

 Reading: John 13:31–38

"By this all men will know that you are my disciples, if you love one another."
John 13:35

This is now the final day's assignment of the six-week video course on Christian caring. We admire you for your tenacity in sticking with the course, even when it got tough. We commend you for setting the time aside and diligently applying yourself to the various activities of the course. We have one final exercise for you.

Read through the following dialogue and jot down in the notes column the principles of caring you have learned as you observe Tom's use of them.

An Example of Caring by Encouragement, Exhortation and Enlightenment

This is an example of a caring encounter, incorporating many of the elements we have looked at during the course. In the column headed Observation Notes, note down the different good aspects of caring that Tom is applying.

Dialogue	Observation Notes
	E.g. Subtle hint Door Opener
Tom: Hello Jim, I haven't seen you in church for a few weeks. How is everything?	
Jim: I've been a bit involved in my business and I'm afraid I've had my nose to the grindstone these past weeks.	
Tom: Been a bit pressured, has it?	
Jim: Yes ... more than I think is good for me really.	
Tom: I think I can understand what you mean Jim, it gets a bit like that for me sometimes. Can you think of any reason why that might be?	
Jim: Well, I'm not sure really. (Pause) ... It does worry me a bit though.	

Observation Notes

Tom: Is it a concern you feel you could share with me, now or at some other time, Jim? I'm a good listener and I care.

Jim: Well, thanks, Tom, it might help if I shared what is on my heart. The truth is, I'm getting a bit too involved in my business and it's beginning to cause problems with my wife and I. She says I'm more concerned about making money than I am about her. She doesn't realise or understand what running a business demands in terms of time ... she never complains about the extra perks the business provides for us, though. Things get a bit difficult between us at times, I must admit.

Tom: It sounds as if you are feeling somewhat frustrated and indignant about that.

Jim: Yes, you could say that.

Tom: Do you think that is the full extent of the problem you are worried about, Jim?

Jim: What do you mean?

Tom: Well, are there any other areas of your life which are being affected by the extra time you are giving to your business?

Jim: It means I can't spend as much time with the children. And of course it cuts into my attendance at church. That's about it really.

Tom: Just to be sure that I don't misunderstand what you are sharing with me, Jim, let me reflect back to you what I am hearing you say: Over the past few weeks, you have been spending a good deal of extra time at your

Observation Notes

business and this is causing a little difficulty between you and your wife. You feel Betty doesn't understand your reasons for the extra time you are putting into your business, even though you have tried to explain them to her, and thus you feel misunderstood. In addition to feeling misunderstood, you are concerned about the way your business interest is cutting into the time you spend with your children and also the way it prevents you from getting to church. This worries you a good deal.

Jim: Yes, I think that's a fair summary of what my concern is, Tom.

Tom: I can see how these concerns must affect you, Jim. Can I share with you some of my thinking on this matter?

Jim: Yes, please do, Tom. I very much appreciate the care and concern you are showing me.

Tom: I've been wondering as we have been talking, Jim, how important is money to you?

Jim: Well, as a matter of fact, it's very important. I grew up in a home where there was little money and a lot of hardship. It makes me feel good when people come to my home and admire our beautiful house, the layout, the furniture and the decor. I'm hoping to build a swimming pool in the garden next year. Then perhaps, in a few years' time, we can move to an even bigger and better house.

Tom: Jim, I get the feeling it's really important to you to make money and display the evidence of your prosperity. I wonder if you would have trouble seeing yourself as a valuable person if you

Observation Notes

didn't have money?

Jim: I hadn't thought of that.

Tom: I am wondering if your drive to work hard, to
          have a successful business and all that it brings
          come from a fear and anxiety that people will
          think less of you if you don't have them. I get
          the feeling that maybe your identity in your own
          mind is linked to your achievement. Do you
          think you are afraid of failure.

Jim: I don't know. I think I would feel very insecure if
          I didn't have money. I think I would fall apart if
          God stripped me of all my material possessions.

Tom: Supposing that were to happen, do you
          think you could trust God with the outcome?

Jim: I don't know, I doubt it.

Tom: Well, Jim should something like that happen
          we know that because of God's purposes it
          would not be hopeless. God knows everything
          that happens to us in life and has promised to
          supply a corresponding source of His grace to
          enable us to handle life's setbacks. He is even
          able to use them as springboards and in the
          process build His character into our lives.
          Look at the cross, what a devastating setback
          that seemed at the time, but God in His purposes
          brought resurrection life out of it.

Jim: I can see what you are saying but it would be
          pretty hard to come to terms with.

Tom: Well, we would all feel pretty hurt if we were
          deprived of material possessions and I am not
          suggesting that God wants to strip you of your

money, but according to Scripture, there is only one sure and reliable way of feeling good about ourselves and that is to recognise that we are complete persons only to the extent that we relate to Christ. Listen to how Colossians 2:10 puts it: "And you are complete in Him, ..." (NKJ) I understand this to be saying that everything we need to function effectively as human beings is to be found in Christ.

Jim: Well, I realise that the Bible says "the love of money is the root of all evil" and we are not to put the love of money before the love of Christ ... is that what you mean?

Tom: Well, that is part of it, but allow me to share with you a verse from Scripture. Jeremiah 2:13 says: "For My people have committed two evils: They have forsaken Me, the fountain of living waters, and hewn themselves cisterns – broken cisterns that can hold no water." (NKJ). God is challenging Israel here with the fact that instead of coming to Him to slake their spiritual thirst, they attempted to have their thirst assuaged through hewing out cisterns, broken cisterns that could hold no water. Can you see any relationship between that text and the things that we are talking about at the moment, Jim?

Jim: I am beginning to see the point you are making, Tom, but I would like you to say a little more before I make any comment.

Tom: I'd be glad to, Jim. All of us have deep longings and deep thirsts within us and one of those longings or thirsts is to be a worthwhile person. But if God is not meeting that thirst or longing, then, because we can only function effectively if it is met, we have to look for some

Observation Notes

other way for that thirst to be assuaged. My guess is that in the past, you have discovered that one way of feeling good about yourself – feeling worthwhile – is to have money. If this is the case, can you see how all your energies have gone into this and how pressured life becomes when we are dependent upon something other than God to meet our deep needs and longings?

Jim: What you say, Tom, certainly makes sense. But help me to understand why I get so upset when my wife does not seem to understand me.

Tom: I'm not an expert in counselling Jim, but as I see it, if your way of finding worth is through money, then any attempt to block that path is going to make you feel terribly threatened and vulnerable. This may be why you get so upset when your wife goes on about you spending too much time at your business. You see, her nagging is a block to your goal of finding worth and value through your ability to make money.

Jim: So what's the answer? Give up trying to make money?

Tom: No, I think the answer lies in a different direction. You need to focus on the fact that all you need to be a worthwhile person is found in Christ. When you discover your true worth in Him, then your will see money in a different light. It will no longer be a demand – but a desire.

Jim: How do I go about finding my worth in Christ rather than in money? Can you help me with this, Tom?

Observation Notes

Tom: It's not going to be easy, Jim, because like us all you have had long experience – in fact a lifetime – of looking in the wrong direction to find your worth. God has been gracious, however, in helping us arrive at a sense of true worth by giving us some clear Scriptures that focus on this. I have discovered in my own life that the more I focus on how much God values me and thinks of me, the more I come to value myself. If you are prepared to spend some time every day meditating on a few Scriptures, I feel sure that you will soon begin to see your true worth and value in the sight of God.

Jim: I most certainly would like to follow your suggestions, Tom. You point me in the direction I should go and I will give the matter my full and complete attention.

Tom: Well Jim, maybe I can describe it in terms of the ABC Theory of Emotions. Let me explain it first and we can see how it applies to you.

Jim: OK.

Tom: The theory is that the circumstances of life do not directly affect the way we feel without first going through our thought processes. *A* equals the life circumstance called the activating event, *C* equals the consequent emotion but *B* equals the belief that we form about the life circumstances that produces the emotion.

Jim: I think I understand.

Tom: Your life circumstance is your excessive commitment to your business and making money. If you slow down or stop being

Observation Notes

successful, your fear and anxiety emerge so you throw yourself into more work, but we know from the theory that you must be saying something to yourself when you slow down and feel the fear and anxiety arising.

Jim: What do you think that might be?

Tom: It could be "If I do not succeed, I will be seen as a less worthwhile person and I cannot bear the thought of being seen as a failure by others." I think that this thought, or something like it, produces the fear and anxiety that drive you on, even to the detriment of your relationship with your wife and children.

Jim: What can I do about it?

Tom: The first thing to recognise is that this is a misbelief, we might even be bold enough to call it a lie. Your value in God's sight does not depend on what you achieve, but who you are Jim. If you are willing to admit your foolish thinking and to accept what God's Word declares about you, your mind will be renewed.

Jim: I'd like to do that.

Tom: Good. I will prepare a list of Scriptures for you and some suggestions on how to meditate on them. I can get these ready for you in a few days' time. Let's plan to get together on Wednesday evening. How would that be?

Jim: That's fine. Oh, one more thing. You said earlier that when I see my true worth in Christ, money will no longer be a demand but desire.

Observation Notes

What did you mean by that?

Tom: Well, up until now, you have been telling yourself that in order to feel worthwhile, you need to have money. As our personality responds very much to what we tell ourselves – "For as he thinks in his heart, so is he" (Proverbs 23:7 NKJ) – whatever we believe or say to ourselves becomes a part of us. The belief you have had that you need money in order to be worthwhile produces a strong demand in your personality – I HAVE TO HAVE MONEY IN ORDER TO FEEL GOOD ABOUT MYSELF. Once you see your true worth does not lie in that direction, then you no longer demand money to meet it. Therefore, money becomes, not a demand, but a desire – something you want but not something you need to keep you together as a person.

Jim: I was interested in that verse you quoted from Proverbs: "For as he thinks in his heart, so is he". I never quite realised before how powerful are the things I say to myself. It's obvious I need to have my ideas straightened out. How do I go about this business of bringing my thinking in line with God's thinking?

Tom: I suggest we make that a subject for future discussion, Jim. In the meantime, begin to focus on the Scriptures, and they will provide the foundation for any further work the Lord has for us to do together. I will look forward to seeing you on Wednesday. Let's pray together and I'll see you then.

How would you rate Tom as a Christian carer?

_____

_____

_____

Well, congratulations on completing the course on Christian Caring, albeit for your final time of group sharing. Our prayer for you is that you will become an instrument of grace, truth and love, and that many lives will be touched and changed because you were willing to give the time and effort to equip yourself more fully for this important ministry of caring.

Prayer: **Father, after this six weeks of training, I offer myself again to You and I place before You all I have sought to learn. Like the boy with the loaves and fishes, bless and multiply my meagre offerings as I make them available afresh to You. Amen.**

Care Practical Application:

_____

_____

_____

Care Group Review

Spend 50–60 minutes interacting together on the responses you have written down in your own personal study.

Spend about 10–12 minutes for each day with each member of the group having an opportunity to reflect and discuss their responses.

Notes on the Discussion

Day 1

_____

_____

_____

Day 2

_____

_____

_____

Day 3

_____

_____

_____

Day 4

_____

_____

_____

Day 5

_____

_____

_____

Share how you are getting on with your Care Practical Application

Conclusions for the week:

_____

_____

_____

_____

_____

_____

Waverley
Training and Events

For more than 20 years CWR has provided biblical training in caring and counselling. Waverley Abbey House was established as a centre for this training in 1987 and today provides a comprehensive range of courses and materials that are taught at Waverley and elsewhere in the UK and overseas. All CWR's counselling courses are validated by the Association of Christian Counsellors (ACC).

Insight Days

Open to all, these one-day seminars give insight into issues such as depression, self-esteem, bereavement, addictions and helping hurting children.

Introduction to Biblical Pastoral Care and Counselling

A five-day course laying the biblical foundations, giving basic skills and a step-by-step approach for pastoral care and counselling. Ideal for those involved in pastoral care, those seeking to test their calling and many others.

Certificate of Christian Counselling (ACC Levels 1 & 2)

This dynamic course introduces you to a counselling model within a biblical framework, together with a range of counselling skills. Excellent for those looking to become better equipped for pastoral care or for their employment, or who seek recognised, professional training to become a counsellor. Available either as day release over one academic year or over ten weekends.

REA
RI

Diploma of Christian Counselling (ACC Level 3)

An advanced course for experienced counsellors designed to develop expertise in a range of complex areas. Available either as day release over one academic year or over ten weekends.

Supervision and Specialist Courses

Training for experienced counsellors in the supervision of others and in areas such as family therapy, addictions, marriage and anger management.

Spiritual Direction

This five-day course enables you to help another person to know God more deeply, practise His presence and yield more fully to His transforming grace.

University Training

In partnership with London School of Theology, courses are offered in Theology and Counselling validated as a Certificate (one year) and Diploma (two year) of Higher Education, or Degree of Brunel University.

Further details

For a FREE course brochure, with details of all these and other courses:

Tel: 01252 784731

Email: training@cwr.org.uk

Website: www.waverley.org.uk

Waverley Training and Events, CWR, Waverley Abbey House, Waverley Lane, Farnham, Surrey GU9 8EP

CRUSADE FOR WORLD REVIVAL
Applying God's Word to everyday life and relationships

The 7 Laws of Spiritual Success

Selwyn Hughes

Just as there are laws in nature that hold our physical world together, so there are laws for life that make our spiritual walk a success. This book is Selwyn Hughes' legacy to future generations and essential reading for anyone who has been inspired by his teaching and ability to apply God's Word to everyday life and relationships.

£7.99 (plus p&p)
ISBN: 1-85345-237-8

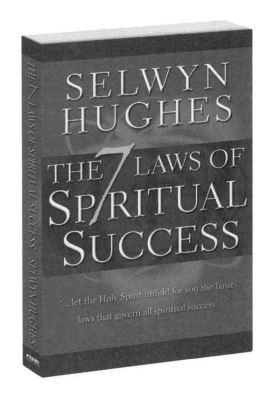

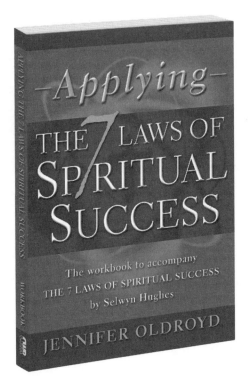

Applying the 7 laws

Jennifer Oldroyd

This workbook, which accompanies Selwyn Hughes' *The 7 Laws of Spiritual Success*, has much to encourage the reading and rereading Selwyn's book. The workbook also has probing questions and action plans to challenge the reader to put into practice Selwyn's teaching and apply it to their daily lives.

£5.99 (plus p&p)
ISBN: 1-85345-297-1

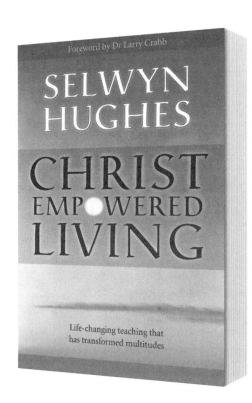

Christ Empowered Living
Selwyn Hughes

Christ Empowered Living is Selwyn Hughes' dynamic core teaching in one easy-to-digest volume. It will transform your life with essential principles of Christian living and help develop your full spiritual potential. Discover biblical insights that will revolutionise your approach to the way you live and help to renew your mind.

This new edition improves readability and gives larger margins for notes.

£7.99 (plus p&p)
ISBN: 1-85345-201-7

Christ Empowered Living Resources Pack

Selwyn Hughes' seminar, Christ Empowered Living, has been turned into an eight-session DVD study course for group or individual use. We are taken on a journey from the Fall to complete restoration as we learn to depend on God and accept Jesus as the power and source of life as God intended. Includes two DVDs and a workbook.

£59.99 (plus p&p)
Code: CELRP

Additional Workbooks Available

£5.99 (plus p&p)
ISBN: 1-85345-328-5

How to Order

The CWR publications featured here are available from Christian bookshops, CWR and their appointed National Distributors and CWR's Online Store at www.cwrstore.org.uk

Prices correct at time of going to press.

Caring God's Way Resources
Additional copies of this workbook and other *Caring God's Way* resources are only available direct from local suppliers or CWR.

National Distributors

UK: (and countries not listed below)
CWR, Waverley Abbey House, Waverley Lane, Farnham, Surrey GU9 8EP. Tel: (01252) 784700 Outside UK (44) 1252 784700

AUSTRALIA: CMC Australasia, PO Box 519, Belmont, Victoria 3216. Tel: (03) 5241 3288

CANADA: Cook Communications Ministries, PO Box 98, 55 Woodslee Avenue, Paris, Ontario. Tel: 1800 263 2664

GHANA: Challenge Enterprises of Ghana, PO Box 5723, Accra. Tel: (021) 222437/223249 Fax: (021) 226227

HONG KONG: Cross Communications Ltd, 1/F, 562A Nathan Road, Kowloon. Tel: 2780 1188 Fax: 2770 6229

INDIA: Crystal Communications, 10-3-18/4/1, East Marredpalli, Secunderabad – 500026. Andhra Pradesh, Tel/Fax: (040) 27737145

KENYA: Keswick Books and Gifts Ltd, PO Box 10242, Nairobi. Tel: (02) 331692/226047 Fax: (02) 728557

MALAYSIA: Salvation Book Centre (M) Sdn Bhd, 23 Jalan SS 2/64, 47300 Petaling Jaya, Selangor.
Tel: (03) 78766411/78766797 Fax: (03) 78757066/78756360

NEW ZEALAND: CMC Australasia, PO Box 36015, Lower Hutt. Tel: 0800 449 408 Fax: 0800 449 049

NIGERIA: FBFM, Helen Baugh House, 96 St Finbarr's College Road, Akoka, Lagos. Tel: (01) 7747429/4700218/825775/827264

PHILIPPINES: OMF Literature Inc, 776 Boni Avenue, Mandaluyong City. Tel: (02) 531 2183 Fax: (02) 531 1960

SINGAPORE: Armour Publishing Pte Ltd, Block 203A Henderson Road, 11–06 Henderson Industrial Park, Singapore 159546.
Tel: 6 276 9976 Fax: 6 276 7564

SOUTH AFRICA: Struik Christian Books, 80 MacKenzie Street, PO Box 1144, Cape Town 8000. Tel: (021) 462 4360 Fax: (021) 461 3612

SRI LANKA: Christombu Books, 27 Hospital Street, Colombo 1. Tel: (01) 433142/328909

TANZANIA: CLC Christian Book Centre, PO Box 1384, Mkwepu Street, Dar es Salaam. Tel/Fax (022) 2119439

USA: Cook Communications Ministries, PO Box 98, 55 Woodslee Avenue, Paris, Ontario, Canada. Tel: 1800 263 2664

ZIMBABWE: Word of Life Books, Shop 4, Memorial Building, 35 S Machel Avenue, Harare. Tel: (04) 781305 Fax: (04) 774739

For email addresses, visit the CWR website: www.cwr.org.uk

CWR is a registered charity – number 294387